Construction risk in river and estuary engineering

A guidance manual

Edited by Mark Morris and Jonathan Simm

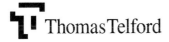

ThomasTelford

Published by Thomas Telford Publishing, Thomas Telford Ltd, 1 Heron Quay, London E14 4JD.

URL: http://www.t-telford.co.uk

Distributors for Thomas Telford books are
USA: ASCE Press, 1801 Alexander Bell Drive, Reston, VA 20191-4400, USA
Japan: Maruzen Co. Ltd, Book Department, 3–10 Nihonbashi 2-chome, Chuo-ku, Tokyo 103
Australia: DA Books and Journals, 648 Whitehorse Road, Mitcham 3132, Victoria

First published 2000

Cover photo provided courtesy of Lewin, Fryer & Partners

A catalogue record for this book is available from the British Library

ISBN: 0 7277 2862 8

Typeset by Apek Digital Imaging, Bristol
Printed and bound in Great Britain by MPG Books, Bodmin, Cornwall

Preface

Civil engineering construction in, or adjacent to, rivers and estuaries is subject to a range of construction risks resulting directly from this environment. Immediately apparent is the risk of flooding but also significant are risks such as scour, poor ground conditions and site drainage, plant operation, site access and tidal impact. Construction works themselves will also have an impact on the river. Such impacts may include an increase in flood water level, changes to the local river regime, scour or siltation, effects on navigation and environmental impacts such as pollution.

Clients, consultants and contractors are becoming increasingly aware of the potential impact that engineering works can have on rivers and the pressure to identify, control and minimise these impacts is growing. Contractors and designers alike, also need to be aware of any potential impacts that their works may have on, or from, rivers and estuaries to ensure that these are taken into account in their temporary and permanent works design.

This manual aims to assist in identifying and taking account of risks in works design and construction. Guidance is offered on risk assessment and management techniques along with the identification of typical risk issues likely to be encountered in the river and estuary environment. Wherever possible, actual case studies have been quoted to demonstrate real and practical issues. Through offering guidance in identifying and assessing risks in a consistent way, this manual should assist in the development of more efficient and cost-effective designs and works.

This manual complements an earlier, more extensive guide, *Construction risk in coastal engineering* (Simm and Cruickshank, 1998), by offering specific advice related to river and estuary issues. As with the coastal manual, guidance is relevant to the civil engineering and contracting industries including consultants, contractors, insurers, researchers, academics, government agencies, local authorities and relevant professional organisations.

Acknowledgements

This manual was produced as the result of an HR Wallingford research project carried out under the Department of the Environment, Transport and the Regions (DETR) — Construction Sponsorship Directorate Partners in Technology Programme. The manual comprises HR Wallingford Strategic Report No. SR562.

We would like to acknowledge key contributions made by persons under the following sections.

Chapter 2	Jonathan Simm and Ian Cruickshank (HR Wallingford) as editors of the *Construction risk in coastal engineering* guide from which this manual has benefited. Ian Meadowcroft (Environment Agency and formally HR Wallingford) and Mark Morris for contributions on risk assessment techniques.
Chapter 3	Mark Morris (HR Wallingford), drawing also on case study material provided by Chris Bown (Lewin, Fryer & Partners), Paul Doughty (Sir Robert McAlpine Ltd), Malcolm Fillingham (Peter Bretts), Andrew Pepper (Environment Agency Advisor) and Sean Kent (Environment Agency).
Chapter 4	David Carter of HSE and Andrew Piechowiak (HR Wallingford).
Chapter 5	Graham Gray (Royal & Sun Alliance).
Chapter 6	Chris Bown (Lewin Fryer & Partners), Sean Kent (Environment Agency), Andrew Piechowiak and Ian Cruickshank (HR Wallingford) and John Strudwick (P. Trant Ltd).
Apendices 1 and 2	As Chapter 2.
Appendix 3	Example risk management workshop facilitated by Jonathan Simm and Ian Cruickshank (HR Wallingford) and attended by: Reg Andrews (J. Murphy & Sons Ltd) Chris Bown (Lewin, Fryer & Partners) Malcolm Fillingham (Peter Bretts) Graham Gray (Royal & Sun Alliance)

	Mark Morris (HR Wallingford)
	Andrew Pepper (Environment Agency Advisor).
Appendix 4	Perrancoombe Stream FAS Case Study material collated by Sean Kent (Environment Agency).
Appendix 5	Prompt lists and tables collated by Pierre Bona and Mark Morris (HR Wallingford).
Appendix 6	As Chapter 4.
Appendix 7	Material collated by Sean Kent (Environment Agency).
Appendix 8	Sourced from the *Construction risk in coastal engineering* guide.

Funding for the project was complemented by in-kind contributions from participating organisations. The following representatives contributed via a Steering Group during the project.

Reg Andrews	J. Murphy & Sons Ltd
Mike Barrett	British Waterways
Chris Bown	Lewin, Fryer & Partners
Paul Doughty	Sir Robert McAlpine Ltd
Gary Edwards	Dean & Dyball Construction Ltd
Malcolm Fillingham	Peter Brett Associates (seconded to Environment Agency)
Graham Gray	Royal & Sun Alliance Insurance plc
Adrian Jackson-Robbins	Davis Longdon Consultancy (representing the DETR)
Sean Kent	Environment Agency
Mark Morris	HR Wallingford Ltd
Ian Padget	WSP International Ltd
Andy Pepper	Environment Agency Flood Defence R&D Topic Advisor
Andrew Piechowiak	HR Wallingford Ltd
Charles Rickard	Mott MacDonald Ltd
Jonathan Simm	HR Wallingford Ltd
John Strudwick	P. Trant Ltd
Mike Pearson	Edmund Nuttall Ltd
David Wood	Henry Boot Construction (UK) Ltd

This guide was edited by Mark Morris and Jonathan Simm of HR Wallingford Ltd.

HR Wallingford is an independent specialist research, consultancy, software and training organisation that has been serving the water and civil engineering industries worldwide for over 50 years in more than 60 countries. We aim to provide appropriate solutions for engineers and managers working in:

- water resources
- irrigation
- groundwater
- urban drainage
- rivers
- tidal waters
- ports and harbours
- coastal waters
- offshore.

Address: HR Wallingford, Howbery Park, Wallingford, Oxon., OX10 8BA, UK

Internet: http://www.hrwallingford.co.uk

Acronyms

ACOP	Approved Code of Practice
APM	Association for Project Management
BODC	British Oceanographic Data Centre
CAR	Construction All Risk
CCT	Compulsory Competitive Tendering
CDM	Construction (Design and Management) Regulations 1994
CERC	Coastal Engineering Research Centre
CIB	Construction Industry Board
CIRIA	Construction Industry Research and Information Association
CM	Construction Management
COPA	Control of Pollution Act
CUR	Centre for Civil Engineering Research and Codes
D&B	Design and Build
DBFO	Design Build Finance Operate
DETR	Department of the Environment, Transport and the Regions
DMC	Design, Manage and Construct
DoE	Department of the Environment (now part of DETR)
DP	Dynamic Positioning
DTI	Department of Trade and Industry
EA	Environment Agency
EC	European Community
ECC	*Engineering and Construction Contract*
EEC	*see* EC
EMV	Expected Monetary Value
EPA	Environmental Protection Act
FDD	Freight Demurrage Defence
FEH	*Flood Estimation Handbook*
FEPA	Food and Environmental Protection Act
FIDIC	Fédération Internationale des Ingénieures Conseils (International Federation of Consulting Engineers)
FSR	*Flood Studies Report*
GRP	Glass Reinforced Plastic
HAT	Highest Astronomical Tide
HSC	Health and Safety Commission
HSE	Health and Safety Executive
HSWA	Health and Safety Act
HW	High Water
ICE 6th	*Institution of Civil Engineers Conditions of Contract,* 6th Edition

ICE	Institution of Civil Engineers
IChem E	Institution of Chemical Engineers
IDB	Internal Drainage Board
ITC	Institute Time Clauses
JCT	Joint Contracts Tribunal
LAT	Lowest Astronomical Tide
LW	Low Water
MAF	Mean Annual Flood
MAFF	Ministry of Agriculture, Fisheries and Food
MAIB	Marine Accident Investigation Branch
MC	Management Contractor
MCA	Maritime and Coastguard Agency
MEPD'B'	Marine Environmental Protection Division
MHWN	Mean High Water Neap
MHWS	Mean High Water Spring
MLWN	Mean Low Water Neap
MLWS	Mean Low Water Spring
MS	Marine Safety
MSA	Marine Safety Agency
MSL	Mean Sea Level
MWL	Mean Water Level
NAABSA	Not Always Afloat But Safely Aground
NEC	*New Engineering Contract* (now revised to ECC)
P&I	Professional & Indemnity
PAGN	Project Appraisal Guidance Notes
PE	Polyethylene
PFI	Private Finance Initiative
PMF	Probable Maximum Flood
POL	Proudman Oceanographic Laboratory
PPPP	Public Private Partnering Programme
PRAM	Project Risk Assessment and Management
RAMP	Risk Analysis and Management for Projects
RISKMAN	Risk Management — the European Project Risk Management Methodology
RFDC	Regional Flood Defence Committees
RIDDOR	Reporting of Injuries, Diseases and Dangerous Occurrences Regulations
SDR	Special Drawing Rights
SFI	Sea Fisheries Inspectorate
SMART	Simple, Measurable, Achievable, Realistic and Time bound
THSD	Trailer, Hopper, Suction, Dredger
TPM	Total Probability Method
VOS	Visual Observations from Ships
VFM	Value For Money
WRC	Water Research Centre

Contents

Illustrations

Boxes

Introduction

1. Introduction

1.1. OVERVIEW

Working conditions created by the river and estuary environment pose a range of new and increased risks to the engineer who wishes to undertake a construction project in this zone. To complete the works successfully the engineer needs to manage these risks such that the works are constructed safely and to specification, ensure the project is undertaken on time and within budget and that any impact on the environment is acceptable. As pressure to reduce costs, increase performance and reduce environmental impacts increases, the consistent and reliable identification and management of project risks is essential.

Construction risk in the river and estuary environment may fall into two categories: risk *from* the environment and risk *to* the environment. An immediately apparent risk from the environment is the risk of flooding but also significant are risks such as scour, poor ground conditions and site drainage, plant operation, site access and tidal impact. Impacts on the environment will include items such as increasing flood water levels, changing the local river regime (leading to scour or siltation), effects on navigation and environmental impacts such as pollution. Clients, contractors and designers alike need to be aware of these risks in order to ensure that they are taken into account in any temporary and permanent works design and works planning.

It is essential that management of and/or containment of identifiable risks be allocated to the organisation most appropriate and able to carry the risk. Seeking to transfer all risks regardless of suitability and cost is unlikely to result in an efficient and cost-effective solution for a construction project.

1.2. AIMS OF THE MANUAL

This manual aims to assist in identifying and managing risks in works design and construction. Guidance is offered on risk assessment and management techniques, along with the identification of typical risk issues likely to be encountered in the river and estuary environment. Through offering guidance in identifying and assessing risks in a consistent way, this manual should assist in the development of more efficient and cost-effective designs and works.

Specifically, this manual aims to:

- illustrate the complexity of risks that are inherent in the construction process to those not familiar with river and estuary engineering

- draw together existing knowledge, experience and research results to give guidance on how best to identify and manage the risks associated with river and estuary engineering
- expose the risks of all parties so that each organisation has a better understanding of the other organisation's risks.

Note that in the commercial environment there are two aspects of risk: commercial and technical. This manual cannot, and does not seek to, supplant commercial decisions but instead seeks to help the decision-making process by better appreciation and evaluation of the technical risks. The manual therefore concentrates on assessment of the typical risks that occur during river and estuary construction projects and the mitigation measures that can be embraced to control or reduce the impact of these risks. Wherever possible, actual case studies have been quoted to demonstrate real and practical issues. By offering guidance in identifying and assessing risks in a consistent way, this manual should assist in the development of more efficient and cost-effective designs and works. The manual assumes that the client has undertaken the necessary project cost-benefit and preliminary risk analyses, and that the river and estuary project is therefore required. Should the reader require further information on the project and organisational aspects that are not covered in this manual, further information can be sought from the following references:

- *Control of risk: a guide to the systematic management of risk from construction* (CIRIA, 1996a). At the time of press, CIRIA was undertaking a research project which follows on from this earlier work and aims to produce a simple risk management software tool for use in the construction industry (CIRIA, 2000)
- *Project appraisal guidance notes* (MAFF, 1993)
- *RISKMAN* (Carter *et al.*, 1995)
- Association of Project Managers' *PRAM guide* (APM, 1997)
- *RAMP* (ICE, 1998).

1.3. SCOPE AND READERSHIP OF THE MANUAL

This manual has been designed for use by a wide readership with a working knowledge of the industry. It is intended to serve the needs of clients, project funders, contractors, consulting engineers (both in a design and supervision role), insurers and those interested with the risks associated with river and estuary engineering.

The manual attempts to provide guidance for both the specialist and non-specialist. In this respect, some of the general information included is intended to educate, for example, a recently graduated engineer, while more specific information is included as a reference for the experienced risk manager. This manager is likely to be found at the 'middle management' level within a contracting organisation or as a project manager within a firm of consulting engineers. While the manual will act as a useful reference on site, the majority of key risk-management decisions should already have been undertaken at earlier stages in the project. The manual is therefore likely to offer the most useful and timely advice in the office environment. The following organisations are likely to find the guide of value.

Project funders, clients, and their representatives for:

- selection of an appropriate procurement process to minimise construction risks
- assessment of design options (starting at the feasibility stage) to reduce construction risks
- optimal apportionment of risk in the contract to the organisation best able to manage it
- assessment of contractor's bids on the basis of expected cost, time, quality, environmental and safety risks.

Contractors for:

- guidance on possible risk assessment processes for the estimating and tendering stages
- risk assessment for alternative designs and working methods
- identification of key risks as they affect the contractor's exposure
- identification of the critical project stages in terms of risk
- identification of the inter-relationship of risks
- identification of appropriate responses to events during construction so as to control and minimise risk.

Designers for:

- assessment of design options for buildability at feasibility stage
- identification and elimination of high risk elements in the design
- carrying out project cost-estimation using cost models
- advising the client on the risk potential associated with the proposed project.

Insurers for:

- assessing the project risks for those parties seeking insurance
- assessing the contractor's ability to identify and control risks
- limiting open-ended liability
- serving the actual needs of the river and estuary construction industry.

Most of the practice and case studies referred to in this manual are drawn from experience gained on projects undertaken within England, and from advice and guidance offered by the Environment Agency (EA) in their role as both environmental regulator and 'client/operator' in England and Wales. While some issues therefore refer specifically to practice in England and Wales the thrust of best practice guidance will be applicable both across the UK and internationally.

1.4. USING THIS MANUAL

Chapter 2 An overview of risk appraisal and management techniques	Chapter 3 A predictable river?
• Definitions used • Guidance on risk mitigation and control strategies • Defining and working to appropriate levels of risk • Risk management for cost and time control • Risk workshops • Comparison of risk assessment and management techniques	• Characteristics of river flow • Predicting fluvial site conditions • Tidal effects • Real-time forecasting • Scour and deposition • Debris • Works location • Environmental risks

APPENDICES

Appendix 1 Steps in the risk identification, assessment and management process	Appendix 2 Other risk assessment and modelling methods	Appendix 3 Example of a risk management workshop	Appendix 4 Case study — Perrancoombe stream flood-area study
• 11 steps for effective identification, assessment and management of risks	• Schematic/ diagrammatic methods • Recording/ presenting risks • Cost and probabilistic methods • Computational risk models	• Workshop structure and agenda • Example case study application • Blank forms for use • Millennium Bridge case study	• Application of CIRIA SP125 techniques by the Environment Agency for budget control on a construction project • Review of analysis before, during and following project completion • Conclusions and recommendations for future application

Chapter 4 Safety	Chapter 5 Insurance	Chapter 6 Procurement
• Legislation for the river and estuary environment • Safety enforcement • Common safety hazards	• Types of insurance • Evaluation of risk in the insurance market • Aide mémoire for insurance issues	• Procurement methods and options • The need to consider and improve procurement strategy • The influence of project funding • Choosing procurement procedure

Appendix 5 River and estuary engineering prompt lists	Appendix 6 Additional health and safety information	Appendix 7 Additional environmental impact information	Appendix 8 Data sources and techniques for predicting tidal water level and wave conditions
• Single-word prompt list • Hazard, consequence, impact and mitigation tables for typical river and estuary risks	• Supporting health and safety information and references	• Supporting environmental impact information and references	• Wind conditions • Offshore waves • Inshore waves • Extreme water levels

An overview of risk appraisal and management techniques

2

2. An overview of risk appraisal and management techniques

2.1. INTRODUCTION

This manual focuses on the risks that occur during river and estuary construction and the mitigation measures that can be embraced to control or reduce the impact of these risks. These mitigation measures may include changes in the way that the project is designed, detailed, procured and managed, right through to the daily site activities and control. As stated in Section 1.2, this manual assumes that a river and estuary project is required and that the client's initial project cost-benefit and business-wide risk analysis has been undertaken.

This section illustrates the various approaches available for risk identification, modelling and management using practical examples from the river and estuary engineering sector. The chapter as a whole builds on many of the concepts set out in CIRIA Special Publication 125, *Control of risk: a guide to the systematic management of risk from construction* (CIRIA, 1996a). Although detailed knowledge of that report may not be essential, it is recommended that the reader refers to it for a greater understanding of risk and the control tools available. These approaches will be useful to client, contractor, designer and insurer at all stages of project development, construction, maintenance and demolition.

There are also legal duties to consider. A co-ordinated approach to many construction projects is needed by all those who can contribute to the avoidance, reduction and control of health and safety risks faced by construction workers and others. This is why the Construction (Design and Management) Regulations 1994 (CDM) place duties on clients, designers, planning supervisors and contractors to consider health and safety at all stages of a project and to manage it effectively. (Further discussion of health and safety issues may be found in Chapter 5.)

It is not possible to give a detailed and prescriptive approach to risk assessment — the variety of projects and perspectives is simply too large. A prescriptive approach would, in any case, tend to bypass or override engineering judgement, expertise and experience, which are all important for effective risk assessment and management.

2.2. THE BENEFITS OF SYSTEMATIC RISK MANAGEMENT IN RIVER AND ESTUARY ENGINEERING

CIRIA (1996a) offers a definition of the benefits of risk management which is summarised here.

Traditionally, risk management has been applied *instinctively*, with risks remaining implicit and managed by judgement informed by experience. *Risk management should make risks explicit, formally describing them and making them easier to manage.* In other words it is a management tool, which for best results requires practical experience and training in the use of appropriate techniques. Once learnt, it supports decision-making and assists instinctive judgement. Fundamentally, risk management helps to:

- identify and question the assumptions that affect the success of the project
- concentrate the effort into controlling the risk through risk prioritisation
- balance the costs and benefits of the risk controlling measures.

Systematic risk management can be undertaken by different organisations at different stages of the project design, development, construction, maintenance and demolition. Examples of risk management at different stages of the project are given below.

By client:

- Strategic assessment of the risks to establish both the overall viability of works and the ability of those works to achieve the client objectives (technical and financial).
- Risk assessment during development and comparison of design options at feasibility stage (e.g. rock mound versus cellular sheet piled wall jetty).
- Optimisation of the apportionment of risk in the contract to the organisation best able to mange it.
- Assessment of bids on the basis of expected cost, time, quality, environmental and safety risks (e.g. comparing the risks associated with a large jack-up barge proposed by one contractor against a floating barge proposed by another).
- Ensuring CDM duties are executed.

By Contractor:

- Creation of basic risk cost model for use in cost estimation and tendering.
- Preparation of a risk/cost profile of alternative designs and working methods.
- Identification of key risks as they affect the contractor's exposure to risk.
- Identification of the critical stages in terms of risk (e.g. by using a risk calendar).
- Identification of the interrelationship of risks.
- Responding appropriately to events during construction to control and minimise risk.
- Ensuring CDM duties are executed.

By Designer:

- Assessment of design options at feasibility stage.

- Identification and elimination of high risk elements of the design (e.g. modification of material specifications to make them easier to obtain).
- Preparation of basic risk cost model for use in project cost-estimation.
- Ensuring CDM duties are executed.

By Insurer:

- Assessment of the project risks which are seeking insurance.
- Assessment of the contractor's ability to identify and control the risks.
- Limiting of any open-ended liability.

Risk management should be instigated right from the feasibility stage of the project's development. The stages and levels of detail appropriate at each stage are discussed in more detail later in this chapter and in Appendix 1.

2.3.   DEFINITIONS USED IN RISK MANAGEMENT

Some terms that are commonly used in risk management are defined overleaf (Box 2.1). Some of these terms, particularly 'risk', have several possible meanings but we have given definitions based on Royal Society, DETR (DoE) and CIRIA guidelines.

2.4.   RISK IDENTIFICATION, ASSESSMENT AND MANAGEMENT

Risk assessment can be undertaken at many different levels. The level of detail, and complexity of the assessment, will depend upon various aspects including:

- project stage
- level of perceived risks
- available time and resources.

This section outlines the 11 steps identified in CIRIA (1996a) for undertaking risk identification, assessment and management. Working through the 11 steps produces a completed *risk register* that not only documents the thought processes but also presents the risk mitigation plans and can be referenced during the review stage. Users should review the risk register prior to any major decisions or changes to the project (e.g. land acquisition, issue and award of tenders).

When considering the application of risk assessment procedures, it should be noted that risk assessment is a process subject to a law of diminishing returns. Users should take care not to prolong risk assessments unduly or it may actually hold up the progress of work rather than assist it. This phenomenon is sometimes known as 'paralysis by analysis'! A balance should be achieved between gain from continued assessment and the cost of further work.

It is also important to recognise the value of a 'top down' approach to risk assessment where risks are initially identified and assessed at a 'high' level (e.g.

Box 2.1. Risk definitions

Hazard: a property or situation that has the potential to cause harm.

Consequences: the adverse effects or harm as the result of realising a hazard which cause the quality of human health, cost, time or the environment to be impaired in the short or longer term.

Risk: a combination of the probability, or frequency, of occurrence of a defined hazard and the magnitude of the consequences of the occurrence.

Probability: is the mathematical expression of chance (for instance, 0·20, equivalent to a 20 per cent or a one in five chance), used wherever there is sufficient data to substantiate it. In many cases, however, it can be no more than the subjective expression of a prospect that may be expressed only qualitatively. The definition applies to the occurrence of a particular event in a given period of time or as one among a number of possible events.

Applying the everyday meaning of estimation and evaluation to the defined meaning of risk leads to further terms and definitions.

Risk estimation: is concerned with the outcome or consequences of a hazard, taking account of the probability of occurrence.

Risk evaluation: is concerned with determining the extent and magnitude of risk and therefore includes an element of risk perception.

Risk perception: is the overall view of risk held by a person or group and includes both feeling and judgement.

Risk assessment: consists of risk estimation and risk evaluation. This definition of risk assessment, by incorporating risk evaluation, goes beyond that in the European Commission Directive 93/67/EEC.

---

delay to project). Once this high level of assessment is complete then it may be appropriate to carry out more detailed assessments at lower, more detailed levels (e.g. project delayed by high river flows preventing delivery of material to site by river).

Figure 2.1 summarises the steps that may be taken for the effective identification, assessment and management of risk. Further details for each step are given in Appendix 1.

2.5. GUIDANCE ON POSSIBLE RISK MITIGATION AND CONTROL STRATEGIES

It is important to recognise that risk mitigation and/or control measures will fall into one or more of the following categories:

- remove
- reduce
- transfer

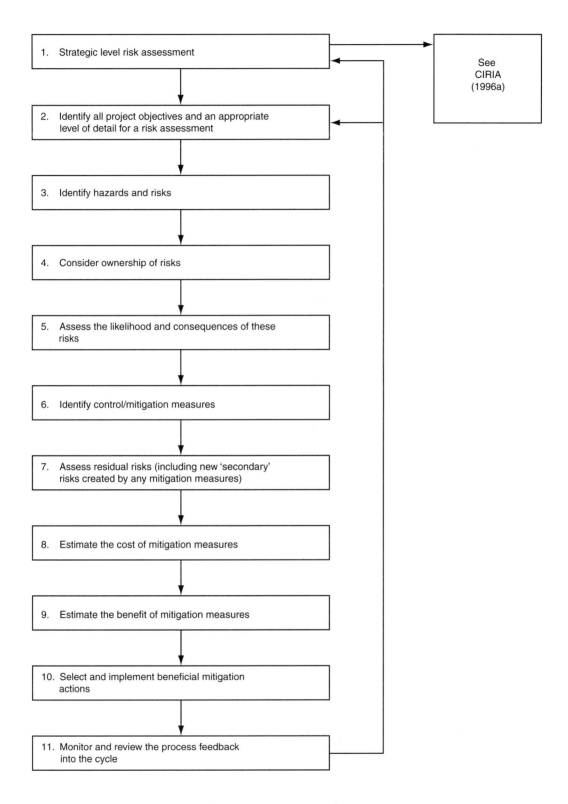

Figure 2.1.   Flow chart of risk management procedure

- share
- insure
- accept.

The optimum control strategy will depend upon, among other factors, the risk, the ability to manage it and the organisations involved. It is not the purpose of this section to define optimum risk control strategies but rather to suggest a range of solutions that may be available, both in terms of proactive and reactive measures. The benefits and disadvantages of the various generic control strategies are discussed below.

Remove
Where possible, risk should be removed. This may be undertaken by redesign or by using a different method of construction. For example:

- using concrete units rather than stone to remove the risk of not being able to obtain stone compliant with the specification
- constructing a training wall from land-based plant rather than water-based plant to remove the river state risk.

However, two significant factors may make this strategy less than ideal:

- The cost or practicality of removing the risk may be far greater or problematic than the actual risk itself (e.g. it may not be practical to completely remove the risk of scour around temporary works).
- The removal of one risk may in itself create another (e.g. constructing works using land-based deliveries and plant may generate a safety risk to the public).

Reduce
Where risk removal is either not possible or not preferred, risk reduction is the next strategy to be considered. This may be through reduction in the hazard, reduction in its probability or through the establishment of a control strategy to limit the consequence. For example:

- making a design specification more flexible to reduce the risk of not being able to obtain materials to meet the specification
- designing temporary works for the diversion of river flow such that they can be quickly removed in the event of an extreme flood so allowing flooding of the works rather than serious flooding of the locality.

Again, caution should be taken as the reduction of one risk may increase the likelihood of other risks or be costly or impractical.

Transfer
This option can be used when an organisation wishes to transfer the risk to another party, usually achieved by means of the contract conditions. For instance,

some clients have transferred the 'unforeseen physical conditions' risk to the contractor. However, it is important to note that *any risk should always be managed by the organisation that is best able to control it.*

It should also be recognised that if an organisation seeks to transfer risks which it is in fact better able to control than the party to whom the risks are being transferred, it will probably end up 'paying' for the risks anyway. Such payment may be in direct increases in time and cost, or decreases in safety or quality, or it may be via the profits and overheads of the organisation that takes the risks.

If it is decided to transfer a risk to another party the following considerations are important:

- Transference of the risk does not remove it and the risk may ultimately return to the originator in the 'unlikely' event that the new risk holder goes bankrupt or the contract is declared unfair in court.
- If the risk transference is from a contractor to a subcontractor, although the primary risk is removed, the contractor will still retain the risk should the subcontractor go bankrupt or fail to deliver.

Share

This option is used in partnering and target-cost type contracts. The aim is to actively involve more than one party with the risk(s) to optimise the risk management and reduce costs. The disadvantages are that:

- one party may still remain partly liable for a risk which it can not actively control
- one of the joint organisations may default, leaving risks and liabilities.

Insure

This option is a form of risk transfer. Insurance is a system whereby in return for the payment of a premium, the few who suffer loss are compensated from the fund contributed to by the many. It is based on the principle of indemnity, which means that a claimant is entitled to have a loss made good but is not allowed to profit by it. Insurance provides a reduction in uncertainty in return for a premium. It is important to recognise that there are certain limitations on insurance as an option:

- Not all risks are insurable. In recent times the insurance market has withdrawn or limited insurance cover with respect to a number of perils (e.g. environmental pollution).
- There is an uncertainty in the premium costs, which can be increased by the insurance company at each renewal date, especially if claims occur.
- Perfect compensation for losses is rarely achieved, as the cost of making a claim, and many other losses including downtime, may be excluded by the insurers.
- The business of an insurance company is ultimately to make a profit from premiums. It is probable that an insured company will ultimately pay for the reduced uncertainty where significant claims are likely.

Note that risks that cannot be totally removed, transferred or insured are sometimes referred to as residual risks. The insurance option is discussed in more detail in Chapter 5.

Accept

Risk acceptance can be either passive or active. Passive acceptance (also referred to as unplanned, unconscious, non-insured) occurs when an organisation is not aware that it is exposed to a risk and consequently takes no action to control it. Examples of passive acceptance occur when:

- specific risks were not identified (since, in practice, it is unlikely that an organisation will identify all the risks)
- the impact of the risk was not correctly assessed
- the control measure was not yet in place.

Active acceptance will occur when an organisation has identified the risk and has made a conscious decision to accept the risk (often on commercial grounds) and pay for it if it occurs. The risk control strategies outlined later in this chapter and in Appendix 2 focus on active acceptance.

2.6. PROJECT MANAGEMENT AND COMMUNICATION

This guide focuses on construction risk management and does not attempt to address the issues of risk related to project management performance. There are already many books available on this topic and these should not be confused with the aim of this guide to focus specifically on construction risk issues.

Good project management and clear lines of communication between all parties on a construction project are essential to minimise the risk of error. Breakdown in communication or unauthorised communication can easily lead to problems (see Box 2.2).

2.7. WORKING WITH APPROPRIATE LEVELS OF RISK

Consider the level of risk assessment applied to a project. If it is sufficiently detailed that specific return period events or probability of occurrences are quoted, then it is logical to ensure that the level of risk accepted is appropriate in relation to the costs and consequences of alternative design or risk conditions. This approach should be applied throughout the project.

2.7.1. What is an appropriate level of risk?

An example of risk consistency may be shown by considering, say, the construction of a bridge pier within a cofferdam at the centre of a river channel.

> **Box 2.2. Maintaining lines of communication**
>
> Familiarity between parties may assist in creating a good working relationship but can inadvertently lead to misunderstandings. A construction project in central Oxford was undertaken for the Environment Agency who employed a firm of consultants to undertake the design and letting of the construction contract. The contractor who was selected opted to subcontract parts of the mechanical and electrical work to two other smaller firms. Coincidentally, representatives from these subcontractors knew the Resident Engineer (RE) supplied by the consultant. Consequently, when on-site and problems arose the subcontractors tended to consult directly with the RE if they were unable to find the site agent easily.
>
> This break in the normal line of communication had two effects. In the short term it tended to allow the quick resolution of problems and eased the progress of work. As such, it appeared beneficial. Problems arose, however, where errors in detailed design meant that modifications had to be made to mechanical and electrical equipment. Without following the formal line of communication the responsibility for and the correct redesign of equipment could easily have formed a serious point for dispute between all parties.

At a basic level, it would be inconsistent to design temporary works to withstand hydraulic loading from a 100-year flood event when, say, the scour protection placed around the works was only designed to withstand flows up to a 50-year flood.

Such a statement assumes, of course, that the risk of failure from each component is similar. For example, if the consequences of failure from hydraulic loading were far more serious than those from failure of the scour protection, then the use of higher design standards for the hydraulic loading design would be appropriate. The issue here is to ensure that any design is appropriate for the level of risk to which it relates.

Often there are many different factors or conditions relating to a project that may be designed to a specified standard, defined to a specific level or exposed to a specific risk. Consider again the construction of a bridge pier and note the following variables in the design process:

- duration of project (increased exposure to occurrence of flood event)
- permitted degree of river blockage by temporary works (based on afflux/backwater level requirements imposed by regulatory authority on a site-specific basis)
- risk of blockage of remaining river cross-section by debris
- design level for flood protection offered by cofferdam (see Box 2.3)
- strength of works to withstand loading during flood conditions.

2.7.2. Allocating an appropriate level of risk

Defining an appropriate level of risk involves:

- calculating the level of risk
- deciding what level of risk is appropriate.

Box 2.3.   Teddington Weir

(Photograph courtesy of A. Pepper)

Plant and works are flooded when river levels exceed design conditions during works at Teddington Weir.

Care should be taken when considering the latter as to whom the risk resides with. 'Appropriate' levels may vary depending upon the risk owner.

Calculating the level of risk

The risk of specific events such as overtopping due to a flood event may be calculated through a relatively simple assessment of probabilities. For a given probability event, there will be a set of conditions such as flow, water level or wave height. To avoid overtopping of temporary works, for example, they should be designed to the maximum level for the chosen probability of event plus any freeboard. Note that for any given event probability, such as a 10-year flood level, there may be a variety of conditions (rainfall intensity and duration, soil moisture deficit, etc.) that could combine to create the event.

Choosing an appropriate level of risk

In recent years, the use of a 1 in 10-year event has been quoted in contracts and insurance policies as an appropriate division level for liability between client and contractor. While moves to define the allocation of risk in this way can only reduce grounds for dispute, and therefore improve conditions, there is still considerable room for better clarification and understanding of the risks posed by specific and combined events. Two issues that should be recognised are the nature of events and their relation to the duration of project works.

Nature of a storm event

The nature of an event can be demonstrated by considering a construction project in a river that relies upon barges to deliver materials to site. The contract states that the contractor will not be liable for costs due to flood events of 1 in 10-years or more. Therefore, when a flood occurs with a flow hydrograph that exceeds the known stage-discharge for a 10-year event the allocation of risk is clear. Classification of the probability of flood event will have been based purely on the value of peak flood discharge. However, what happens when high or low flow occurs in the river for an abnormally long period? Consider an abnormally long flood event with a peak discharge matching that of, say, a 1 in 8-year flood. According to the contract terms responsibility for this event would fall with the contractor. The abnormal duration of the flood flow, however, would mean that the true probability of occurrence for this event would probably exceed 1 in 10-years and the disruption caused to the contractor would probably justify compensation.

The way in which such problems could be avoided is to consider all ways in which weather conditions may affect a project. This should include all effects such as the possibility of both high and low river flows, water levels and waves, along with the impact of their short or long-term duration. It is essential that an appropriate level of risk is identified and agreed at the procurement stage rather than later in the project.

The duration of project works

It is not possible to simply state an event return period within a contract, without considering the duration of the project works themselves. If this is done then the level of risk allocated between client and contractor will vary with each project (see examples in Boxes 2.4 and 2.5).

The probability of a storm event matching or exceeding a specified return period during a given period of time may be calculated by:

$$P = 1 - [1 - 1/T]^n$$

where P = probability of exceedence
T = return period of specified event (e.g. 1 in 10-year event)
n = given period of time (i.e. project duration)

Note that the techniques presented here assume an even distribution of flood risk during the construction period. Depending upon the catchment location, it is likely that there will be a greater or lesser risk of flood events during both the summer as well as winter periods.

Statistics can also be misleading. Note that if a project is of short duration, the likelihood of an event occurring may be reduced but the impact on the project of that event is likely to be much greater. A delay of one week during a month-long project constitutes a 23% delay. A delay of a week during a year-long project is only a 2% delay. A more detailed explanation of these techniques and equations may be found in Wilson (1990).

Box 2.4. An example of risk variation with project duration

Consider how the level of risk defined by contract may vary if, for example, a 1 in 10-year condition was stipulated for projects with a 1-year duration and a 1-month duration.

The probability of a 1 in 10-year event, or greater, occurring during the 1-year project may be calculated as:

$$P = 1 - [1 - 1/T]^n = 1 - [1 - 1/10]^1 = 0{\cdot}1 \text{ or } 10\%$$

For the same event to occur during a 1-month project:

$$P = 1 - [1 - 1/T]^n = 1 - [1 - 1/10]^{1/12} = 0{\cdot}009 \text{ or } 0{\cdot}9\%$$

Looking at this from another angle, what storm event should be defined within the contract for a 1-month project to allocate the same level of risk between client and contractor compared to a 1-year project with a 1 in 10-year event specified?

From the above equation, T may be calculated:

$$T = 1/[1 - (1 - P)^{1/n}]$$

Given that $P = 0{\cdot}1$ and $n = 1/12$ then $T = 1{\cdot}4$ years.

While the calculation of a 1·4-year event may seem low, it is logical and is supported by the experience of contractors.

The third parameter, namely n, the project duration, may also be calculated should the other two parameters be specified. For example, how long could a project run if you were prepared to accept a 20% risk of the 1 in 10-year event occurring during the construction period?

Rearranging the above equation gives the following solution in terms of n:

$$n = \log[1 - P]/\log[(T - 1)/T]$$

Given that $P = 0{\cdot}2$ and $T = 10$ then $n = 2{\cdot}1$.

For these conditions your construction project could run for an estimated 2·1 years.

Box 2.5. Rare events do happen

To ensure that the new Inverness rail viaduct would not be undermined by the lowering of bed levels (as with the original), construction of the bridge was preceded by the construction of a weir just downstream of the site. The weir was constructed by driving sheet piling across the river and placing protection in the form of 2 tonne stone blocks, 1·5 m deep, across the bed downstream. Driving the piles and placing the stone was scheduled to take no longer than one week. Between driving the piles and placing the stone protection a 1 in 5-year flood occurred that created scour holes up to 8 m deep downstream of the piles, almost leading to failure of the structure.

The probability of occurrence was approximately:

$$P = 1 - [1 - 1/T]^n = 1 - [1 - 1/5]^{(5/365)} = 0{\cdot}3\% \text{ (!)}$$

For quick reference Table 2.1 shows how the storm return-period event would change with project duration, assuming a constant risk division of 0·1 (i.e. $P = 0{\cdot}1$ — the client takes a 10% chance of paying for delays/damage due to a flood event).

Table 2.1. Storm event in relation to project duration for a fixed probability of occurrence

Project duration: n	Storm event: T
1 month	1·4 yrs
2 months	2·1 yrs
3 months	2·9 yrs
6 months	5·3 yrs
9 months	7·6 yrs
12 months	10 yrs
18 months	14·7 yrs
24 months	19·5 yrs
36 months	29 yrs
60 months	50 yrs

In conclusion, to ensure an appropriate level of risk one should:

- consider how weather variations may affect your project in terms of magnitude and duration
- consider the duration of the project
- consider an acceptable level of risk for the project
- back calculate and agree appropriate weather conditions during procurement.

2.8. RISK MANAGEMENT FOR COST AND TIME CONTROL

Both clients and contractors will wish to make estimates of the likely additional costs and/or time they may incur on river and estuary engineering construction projects due to risk factors.

Clients will wish to do this in order to ensure that they have allocated an appropriate budget and time frame for the project. Their motives for this will reflect the nature of the client:

- Private sector clients will wish to estimate risk budgets because the overall project budget may affect the project viability or timing.
- Public sector clients will wish to estimate risk budgets because they will need to forecast expenditure profiles and because budgets may be constrained by the availability of funding and/or benefit-cost analysis.

Contractors will wish to make estimates of risk costs and construction duration to ensure that they make an adequate profit on the project, or at least do not make an unforeseen loss.

Historically, contractors have built up their cost contingencies in two stages. The first stage is embedded within the initial estimating process. The estimator, often instinctively, includes uncertainty when making an assessment of plant, materials and labour for a project. For example, the estimator may include:

- a percentage of material wastage

- costs of delays, when deciding on unit prices for materials
- downtime and/or spare plant, when deciding on hourly rates for plant.

The second stage is usually undertaken at a more senior level, immediately prior to submission of tenders. Here the estimators' allowances are tested by the project team and modifications/additions are made to take account of factors that have been over or under-estimated and factors that have previously been ignored. This process involves a great deal of judgement and is significantly influenced by commercial factors, including the extent to which it is desirable for the contractor to win the particular project.

Contractors are now becoming more rigorous in their approach to risk in estimating and use a wide range of tools to assist them, including both cost-risk and schedule-risk models. However, these tools are only an aid to decision making and should never entirely supplant experience and judgement.

Clients can and should also make use of these tools in setting project budgets that reflect a realistic estimate of final out-turn costs. In doing so, clients often have the advantage over contractors, in that they can prepare their cost budgets and time estimates over a much longer time scale than is available to contractors during tendering and hence there is the opportunity for more careful evaluation of the risks. On the other hand, clients may need some contractor guidance to ensure that their estimates are realistic; despite the potential difficulties, this advice should always be sought if possible.

2.8.1. Methods for estimating total project budgets

Many methods are presently available for estimating project budgets. These are discussed briefly in the next section and in more detail in Appendix 2.

For most river and estuary engineering projects, it is recommended that attention should be focused on three potential methods, two of which are now being adopted by the Environment Agency (see Box 2.7).

(a) The simplest method recommended (CPM 3 in Table 2.5), involves preparing a risk register in which *each risk is represented by a single probability and lump sum price for the consequence*. The expected value of the risk for that item is the sum of its probability and consequential cost and the total risk budget is then just the sum of these items. This approach is illustrated in Table 2.2 where it will be noted that the risk register also includes revised costs and probabilities based on the effect of proposed risk mitigation measures.

(b) The next method is only slightly more complicated (CPM 5 in Table 2.5) and involves *a more systematic description of all risks based on separate identifiable consequences (e.g. none, marginal, severe)* as shown by the example in Table 2.3. When combined with the basic price for an element of work these are often described as: minimum, most likely, maximum. The probability of all the consequences should add up to 100% to cover all reasonable eventualities, excluding *force majeur* situations. This method

Table 2.2. Part of a risk register or portfolio with assessment of risk cost

		Initial risk							Mitigation			
Column 1	Column 2	Column 3	Column 4	Column 5	Column 6	Column 7	Column 8	Column 9	Column 10	Column 11	Column 12	Column 13
Element	Risk	Owner	Likelihood	Con-sequences	Assessment	Mitigation measure	Mitigation by whom	Mitigation when	Revised likelihood	Revised con-sequences	Revised assessment	Cost of mitigation/ comment
Drive sheet piled wall from marine pontoon	Piles not arrived on site	Contractor	10%	£10 000	£1000	Pre-order providing time float	Contractor	On award	2%	£10 000	£200 (none)	None
	High river flows preventing positioning/ driving	Contractor	5%	£20 000	£1000	Purchase additional anchors if required	Contractor	On receipt of flood warning	2%	£20 000	£400 (£350)	£350
	Hard ground conditions/ obstructions	Client	20%	£30 000	£6000	Drive additional boreholes at Ch 60–90 m	Client	Pre-award	10%	£20 000	£2000 (£6000)	£6000
	Etc.											

Table 2.2. continued

	Initial risk						Mitigation					
Column 1	Column 2	Column 3	Column 4	Column 5	Column 6	Column 7	Column 8	Column 9	Column 10	Column 11	Column 12	Column 13
Element	Risk	Owner	Likelihood	Consequences	Assessment	Mitigation measure	Mitigation by whom	Mitigation when	Revised likelihood	Revised consequences	Revised assessment	Cost of mitigation/comment
Dredge in front of new wall	Dredger not available	Contractor/Subcontractor	10%	£10 000	£1000	Confirm commencement date	Contractor	On award	5%	£10 000	£500 (none)	None
	Low river flows preventing access	Contractor	2%	£10 000	£200	Use land-based plant if required	Contractor	Monitor when flows reduce	1%	£10 000	£100 (none as already on site)	None as already on site
	Contaminated sediments	Client	35%	£20 000	£7000	Carry out additional sediment analysis	Client	Pre-award	10%	£20 000	£2000 (£500)	£500
	Ordnance found	Contractor	10%	£30 000	£3000	Carry out magneto-meter surveys and warn personnel/place in H&S plan	Contractor	On award and during contract	2%	£30 000	£600 (£450)	£450
Etc.												

Table 2.3. Part of a risk register or portfolio with a systematic method of risk assessment

	Initial risk						Mitigation
Column 1	*Column 2*	*Column 3*	*Column 4*	*Column 5*	*Column 6*	*Column 7*	*Column 8*
Element	Risk	Owner	Level	Likelihood	Con-sequences	Risk value	Etc.
Drive sheet piled wall from marine pontoon	Piles not arrived on site	Contractor	None	90%	£0	£0	
			Marginal	8%	£10 000	£800	
			Severe	2%	£15 000	£300	
	High river flows preventing positioning/ driving	Contractor	None	95%	£0	£0	
			Marginal	4%	£20 000	£800	
			Severe	1%	£1 000 000	£10 000	
	Etc.						

more accurately captures the risks and has the benefit of encouraging completeness, but does require a little more assessment.

The Expected Monetary Value (EMV) of risks can then be obtained by summing the risk values (£11 900 for Column 7 of Table 2.3).

(c) The final method is to use the *Monte Carlo analysis technique.*

This technique provides a mechanism for calculating a risk distribution from a given set of risk elements. The procedure is computational and may be applied when the number and/or interaction between risk elements is such that a hand calculation would be difficult or time consuming.

Monte Carlo methods are exceptionally flexible and powerful, and can be adapted for use with all types of model and any probability distribution. They are also very simple to implement, especially since user-friendly software 'add-ins' to spreadsheets are now available.

The technique involves first defining a probability distribution (i.e. the possible events with their probability and consequence). This probability distribution can be as simple as that defined by the minimum, most likely and maximum prices and probabilities under the previous method (systematic description of risks). The technique then works by sampling this distribution repeatedly. During each sample a possible sequence of events is selected, with a defined outcome. By repeating the sampling procedure many times a set of results is built up that is statistically similar to the defined risk conditions. The technique may be applied to variables such as time as well as cost. A simple example is given in Box 2.6.

The main drawback is that many samples and simulations may be required to arrive at a reliable result because the method is based on random sampling.

Box 2.6. Simple example of the Monte Carlo process

Building on the systematic description of risks in Table 2.3, risks may be identified and summarised as shown in Table 2.4

Table 2.4. Example risk register

Risk	Level	Probability	Consequence
Risk 1 Ordnance found in river bed	None Marginal Severe	75% 20% 5%	£0 £20 000 £40 000
Risk 2 Estuary bed level change	None Marginal Severe	85% 10% 5%	£0 £30 000 £40 000
Risk 3 Delay in supply of piles	None Marginal Severe	90% 8% 2%	£0 £10 000 £15 000
Risk 4 etc.			

Monte Carlo simulation is then used to carry out a series of discrete samples to simulate the different possible scenarios weighted according to the relative probabilities of occurrence (i.e. three quarters of the runs will sample none in Risk 1). For example the first two runs may be as follows:

First run: Risk 1   £0
               Risk 2   £20 000
               Risk 3   £0
                     Total   £20 000

Second run: Risk 1   £40 000
               Risk 2   £0
               Risk 3   £0
                     Total   £40 000

After just two runs the possible risk amounts that have been produced are £20 000 and £40 000. Ideally, after many more runs a spread of risk, as shown in Figure 2.2, may be obtained.

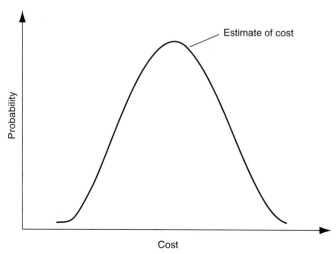

Figure 2.2. Example probability — cost distribution

This is particularly true if there are many variables and if rare, infrequently-sampled events are of interest. Monte Carlo methods can include correlation, where one sampled value can affect the likelihood of another variable, as is often the case in real world situations. However, the values of correlation coefficients may be difficult to derive or estimate for all but the most obvious cases.

Monte Carlo methods may allow an underestimation of uncertainties because, in most applications, it is assumed that the form and parameters of probability distributions are known, as is the correlation between parameters. The system does, however, allow for sensitivity analyses to be undertaken relatively easily. Once the 'base' parameters have been established the probability distributions may be modified to assess the overall impact they may have on the project.

Appendix 4 details a case study application of CIRIA (1996a) techniques in which Monte Carlo techniques have been applied for budget forecast and control on a real construction project.

2.8.2. Risk management for budgetary control within the Environment Agency

The Environment Agency are now following the kind of tiered approach described in the previous section (with analysis depending on the level of risk and project complexity). To support this approach they have prepared a guidance document *Risk assessment and management (guidance for the assessment and management of risks in project management for engineering works)* (Environment Agency, 1997a). An extract from this advice is given in Box 2.7. Note, however, that their guidance applies only to budgetary analysis/control from a client's viewpoint.

Box 2.7.   Environment Agency guidance on residual risks and contingencies

The Environment Agency has provided recommendations for client budgetary risk assessment and control, and has developed the following basic set of rules for the assessment of financial contingencies on projects such as river and estuary engineering schemes:

1. If the potential impact of the residual risks is small, then it may be appropriate to allow a 10% contingency. However, it is advisable to develop confidence in the value of contingency allowed using the following process.
2. Firstly, residual risks should be assessed for a numerical probability of occurrence and the consequences of occurrence valued in £000s. This should be repeated for all the residual risks.
3. A Simple Probabilistic Analysis should be obtained from the product of these values, summed for all of the residual risks to provide an Average Risk Estimate. The estimate so obtained should then be considered against the value of works.
4. If the value is less than 12·5% of works value, a 10% contingency is probably appropriate. If the value is between 12·5% and 20% then the actual % should be considered for the contingency.

> **Box 2.7. continued**
>
> 5. If, however, the value is greater than 20%, this simple method may not provide sufficient confidence and an assessment using software, based on the Monte Carlo Simulation Approach should be carried out. This will define 50% and 95% confidence limits to the potential additional cost. 50% confidence represents the most likely value for contingencies (95% gives a reasonable upper limit to additional cost).
> 6. It is recommended that project contingencies at 50% confidence level are added to the works cost in the calculation of total project cost.
>
> (The estimated project cost including contingencies at 95% confidence limit should be compared to the benefits of the project to ascertain robustness of justification.) If, during the assessment of the consequential costs, it is apparent that particular risks have a disproportionate effect on the contingency value, then the control actions for those risks should be reviewed to seek opportunities for more effective control or to improve the confidence in the value of contingencies applied. This process will reduce the impact of risks but will not remove the risks themselves.

2.9. RISK WORKSHOPS

Risk workshops are a valuable and recommended method for:

- introducing the project team
- demonstrating clear intent to identify and manage risks rigorously
- identifying project aims and objectives
- identifying project risks
- creating risk portfolios (which includes risk identification, ownership, mitigation measures etc.).

The various stages in a risk management workshop may be broadly defined as follows:

(*a*) Introductions
(*b*) Agreement of workshop aims and objectives
(*c*) Agreement of project aims and objectives
(*d*) Prioritisation of project objectives
(*e*) Identification of project risks:

  (i)   long list
  (ii) short list
  (iii) prioritise
  (iv) consolidate

(*f*) Generation of risk portfolio
(*g*) Follow up tasks such as the development of:

  (i) Cost plan
  (ii) Risk calendar

(iii) Project contingencies

(iv) Risk register

An example workshop is presented in detail under Appendix 3. This example works through each of the above stages, except for the follow up tasks. Since the example project was based around a real construction project three different sets of conclusions are presented for comparison. These are:

(*a*) the participants' initial 'gut feel' for the project — prior to the risk workshop

(*b*) conclusions drawn from the risk workshop

(*c*) key issues that were identified or arose during the real construction project.

It is becoming increasingly common, and good practice, to undertake and often combine both risk management and value management workshops.

2.10. OTHER RISK ASSESSMENT AND MODELLING METHODS

A wide range of other risk assessment and modelling methods are available. In addition to those already described in Sections 2.8 and 2.9 above, these include:

(*a*) Schematic/diagrammatic methods

   (i)   Influence diagrams and rich pictures
   (ii) Likelihood — consequence tables
   (iii) Flow diagrams
   (iv) Decision event trees
   (v)   Risk calendars

(*b*) Recording risks and control strategies

   (i)   Risk registers
   (ii) Strategy summary

(*c*) Other cost and probabilistic methods

   (i)   Percentage/lump sum to tender value
   (ii) Risk register with percentage/lump sum per item
   (iii) Risk register with percentage/lump sum against a spread of risk probabilities per item
   (iv) Total Probability Method

(*d*) Computational risk models

Table 2.5 summarises these various risk assessment and modelling techniques detailed within this chapter, with guidance on where each approach may be most

Table 2.5. A summary of comparison of risk assessment and management techniques

Technique	Typical application
Schematic/diagrammatic methods	
Influence diagrams and rich pictures	For project planning stage to identify tasks and relationships
Likelihood — consequence tables	For initial or rough assessment of risk
Flow diagrams	Summarise stages in a given process. Records and considers options for what-if scenarios
Decision event trees	Considers all possible events and allocates probabilities to occurrence. Apply to small/medium projects or breakdown into tasks
Risk calendars	Summary document suitable for medium/large projects
Recording risks and control strategies	
Risk registers	Summary of risk and management/mitigation measures. Appropriate for use on all medium/large projects
Strategy summary	A summary showing risk control strategies applicable to all projects
Cost and probabilistic methods	
CMP1 Percentage/lump sum to tender value	Appropriate when undertaking a familiar task, with good knowledge of the area and limited time or need to assess risks
CPM2 Risk register with percentage/lump sum per item	Appropriate when undertaking a familiar task, with good knowledge of the area and limited time or need to assess risks
CPM3 Risk register with percentage/lump sum plus probability of occurrence per item	Appropriate when undertaking a familiar task, with good knowledge of the area and limited time or need to assess risks — *preferred method* where contingency not more than 10% of project value. If higher suggest use of CPM7. If less than 15% CPM5 may be suitable
CPM4 Risk register with percentage/lump sum against a spread of risk probabilities per item	More elaborate version of CPM3. Better to use CPM7
CPM5 Systematic capture of all risks to obtain expected monetary value of risks	Appropriate for cost control on projects. Further improvement on CPM3
CPM6 Total Probability Method (TPM) — Probability distribution method 1	More precise than methods CPM1 to CPM5. Appropriate for cost and scheduling control on projects with multiple and interactive risks
CPM7 Monte Carlo analysis — Probability distribution method 2	More precise than methods CPM 1 to CPM5. Appropriate for cost and scheduling control on projects with multiple and interactive risks
Computational risk models	
Cost risk techniques	Appropriate when an elaborate cost model is required, based on the normal schedule of rates and quantities associated with a bill of quantities. In addition to rates and quantities the cost-risk model includes information on uncertainties in unit rates and quantities. Also includes risk items as per CPM5, CPM6 and CPM7
Schedule risk techniques	Appropriate when it is desired to estimate the likely time to achieve project milestones and project completion and where there are complex interrelationships between the activities and associated likely variations in the critical path
Scenario modelling	Appropriate when the detail of consequences of difference scenarios and decisions are needed. Scenarios could include floods or accidents. Based on time modelling but can give cost consequences
Real time modelling	Appropriate when forecasting likely consequences of prevailing conditions and decision options
Risk workshops	
Risk workshops	Suitable for all medium/large projects where multiple risks exist with a variety of owners

Advantages	Disadvantages
Provides a mechanism for recording ideas and thoughts for a project during brainstorming type sessions	
Allows an indication of risk level without becoming preoccupied with specific risk probabilities	
Provides a graphic representation of a process to aid project management	Suitable for specific problems only. Diagram for entire projects becomes too large and complex for easy use
Provides a summary of possible options. Identifies probability of occurrence. Highlights links and sequences within a task	Can become very complex for large projects and interrelated tasks
Indicates at a glance the risk level associated with a particular activity	Requires continual updating
Provides a clear and easily traceable record of risk management actions	Requires continual updating
Provides a single-sheet quick reference of risk management techniques for the project	
Quick and simple	Relies solely on engineering judgement. Is not necessarily consistent or traceable
Relatively quick. Identifies key risk items	Relies heavily on engineering judgement for each task
Relatively quick. Identifies and quantifies risk budget	Relies heavily on engineering judgement. Takes no account of risk variability
Relatively quick. Takes some account of risk variability. Identifies and quantifies risk budget	Still relies heavily on engineering judgement. Approach to risk variability of limited value
Allows a more precise estimate of the likelihood of project costs, taking realistic account of risk variability	Becomes difficult with multiple tasks and interrelated risks
Simple to apply where number of risks is limited. Avoids sampling errors that may arise with Monte Carlo Simulation (CPM7)	Becomes very complicated to apply with large numbers of combinations of risks and risk categories. CPM7 preferred normally
Allows an estimate of the likelihood of project costs, timing, etc. Allows sensitivity analyses to be made on specific components of a project	Requires the use of computer spreadsheets or models for analysis. Multiple runs will be required to ensure a suitable level of accuracy. Requires a numerical estimate of risk probability and impact for each event
Allows a much more detailed cost model to be prepared. Automated proprietary software can be used	Time consuming to set up in a robust manner. May add little additional value to civil engineering projects where the number of work items is limited
Allows detailed planning based on activity networks generating resultant likely programs in graphical form. Automated proprietary software available	Time consuming to set up in a robust manner, especially where there are embedded cycles of operation. May add little additional value where the project critical path is fixed due to the limited number of activities
Model can be run repeatedly to obtain range of possible outcomes. Can be used for decision support to support evaluation of 'what-if' scenarios	Time consuming to set up in a robust manner
Can be based on an existing scenario model	Time consuming to set up in a robust manner. Uncertainty about whether all relevant factors have been included
Promotes team working. Identifies risk items and management and mitigation measures. Builds a framework for the management of risks throughout the project	Requires co-operation from all parties involved with the project. (It is recognised that this may be difficult at the early stages of a project but this is when the greatest benefits may be achieved)

suitable for application and a summary of advantages and disadvantages of each technique. Please note that this guidance is based on a general approach and specific project characteristics may make alternative techniques more appropriate than those recommended.

Further details of these techniques are given in Appendix 2, together with references for further reading.

A predictable river?

3

3. A predictable river?

A river may, in an extreme situation, change from a calm steady flow to a raging torrent carrying sediment and debris in only a few minutes. Being prepared for such changes requires an ability to both identify the potential behaviour of the river and to predict the likelihood and impact on construction works of such conditions. Many techniques exist for the prediction of river conditions and often do not require expensive studies to produce reasonable answers. However, as with all risk assessment procedures, a balance must be sought between the cost of analysis and the value that it may bring to the project.

The following sections fall into three broad categories: firstly river characteristics and how their magnitude and impact may be assessed, secondly interaction of construction work with the river and finally, environmental risks. The section on environmental risk is intended to highlight environmental issues that may impact on construction projects, rather than construction work that impacts on the environment. The latter topic justifies a text in its own right, which is not covered within this manual (references to other texts may be found in Appendix 7).

3.1. CHARACTERISTICS OF RIVER FLOW

River flooding is the most common cause of disturbance for a river engineering construction project. For a flood event the following features should be considered:

- magnitude — both in terms of duration and water level
- rate of increase in flow/water level
- velocity of flow
- changing pattern of currents
- local effects — waves, etc.
- areal extent of inundation.

Magnitude
Flood events are normally defined in size by their return period. For example, a 1 in 10-year flood is, on average, likely to be exceeded once in every ten years. Since this is a statistically-based description, this does not prevent such events occurring more or less frequently than the quoted return period. This is a common misconception held by many people unfamiliar with statistical or risk terminology.

It should be recognised that there are many factors that contribute to any given flood event. For example, the flood may be of relatively small flood discharge but for an abnormally prolonged period. Equally, it may be a 'flash flood' where a very large discharge occurs rapidly but for only a short period of time. The nature of the flood is therefore likely to have a significant effect on the construction programme. If the allocation of risk defined within a contract is based on a value of river discharge, the contractor may find himself liable for project delays due to prolonged periods of flow that, while they may not exceed the defined limits, do constitute an extreme event by their prolonged duration. If liability is based on a return period event the various permutations of flow, level and duration should be considered (see Section 2.7.2).

Rate of increase in flow/water level

The speed with which flow in a river will respond to heavy rainfall will depend upon the size and nature of its catchment. Typically small, steep and urbanised catchments will result in rapid runoff with the potential for flash flooding of the works. Conversely, large, flat and rural catchments may take a number of days to respond to rainfall events.

The speed of response will be particularly relevant where construction works partially or completely block the river. Under these conditions the river flow may be diverted or limited to a reduced section of the original channel. It is common for a regulatory authority to allow partial constriction of a channel, providing the obstruction can be removed when required in advance of extreme flood events. The speed with which the works may need to be 'opened' will be directly linked to the response of the river and catchment.

Velocity of flow

The velocity of flow in the river will depend upon the nature of the river as well as the magnitude of the storm event. The flow velocity will directly affect the degree, if any, of scouring that may occur around any temporary or permanent works. Local scour caused during flood events is a common cause of the failure of temporary works, which by their very presence may have increased velocities and altered flow patterns.

Changing pattern of currents

During a flood event, and especially if the river flows out of bank, the pattern of flow in the river channel may change significantly. Consideration should be given to identifying likely or possible changes to the main direction of flow adjacent to any works and the design of any protection necessary to protect the works during such conditions.

Local effects

During flood events, it is possible for flow patterns to change and for local super-elevation of water level and waves to occur. Depending upon the nature of the river, waves of appreciable height (both standing and moving) may form and should be considered when planning the works.

3.2. PREDICTING FLUVIAL SITE CONDITIONS

There are a range of techniques and information sources that may be used for estimating how river conditions could vary during a construction project. The sections below identify a number of these.

3.2.1. Data records

Gauging station data

The Environment Agency maintains a network of flow gauging stations in England and Wales and data from these stations are recorded at a central location, CEH Wallingford (formerly the Institute of Hydrology), where they are statistically analysed.* CEH Wallingford also collates flow data from Scotland and Northern Ireland. The age and, hence, duration of data for any given site varies, but it is accepted that recorded data is far more reliable than theoretical estimates. A summary of all gauging station locations along with the data collected (maximum, minimum, peak flows, etc.) is presented in a report published periodically by the Institute of Hydrology (in the future by CEH Wallingford) called *Hydrological data, UK (Hydrometric register and statistics)*.

Data records (time series and statistics) for specific gauging station sites may also be obtained directly from CEH Wallingford. When overseas, similar data should be available from comparable government offices.

Potential flood limits — Section 105 survey data

Under Section 105 of the Water Resources Act 1991 the Environment Agency has undertaken a nationwide programme of survey work and analysis to determine the likely flood extents along all 'main' rivers during 100-year flood events. The function of the flood plans is to assist with planning control in river floodplains. Where a development activity falls within this zone, the planning authority is obliged to seek the views of the Agency on planning consent. Section 105 of the Water Resources Act 1991 replaced Section 24(3) of the 1974 Water Act. Some data from Section 24(3) plans may be available or may be included within the Section 105 plans.

Plans showing these flooded outlines should be available from regional offices of the Environment Agency. It should be noted, however, that the accuracy of these plans will vary from catchment to catchment. The plans are indicative only. Definitive studies should be undertaken for specific developments, particularly when these are in urban areas.

3.2.2. Hand calculations

Knowledge of typical water levels, and how they may vary, at a site is likely to be a primary issue. If flow data, rather than level data, is available for a site then

---

* CEH Wallingford (formerly the Institute of Hydrology) may be contacted at the following address: CEH Wallingford, Wallingford, Oxfordshire, OX10 8BB. Tel: 01491 838800, Fax: 01491 692424, Website: www.ceh.ac.uk and www.ceh.ac.uk/ih

the water level for a given flow may be estimated using simple hand calculations.

If the reach of a river is not affected by any downstream structures then the flow may be considered to be under 'normal' flow conditions. In this situation, Manning's Equation may be applied to predict water level or discharge.

Manning's Equation may be written as:

$$Q = \frac{(A^{5/3}/P^{2/3})S_o^{1/2}}{n}$$

where A = flow area (m^2)
        P = wetted perimeter of flow area (m)
        S_o = slope of bed
        n = Manning's n value for roughness

The form and application of this equation may be found in most standard texts on hydraulics such as Chadwick (1995) and Chow (1973). The equation depends greatly upon the selection of an appropriate channel roughness coefficient, n. Chow (1973) offers advice on the selection of this value through channel description and photos.

If water levels at the site are affected by a structure, such as a weir or a bridge, then Manning's Equation is not appropriate since the flow is not under 'normal' conditions. Water levels at the weir or bridge will be determined by the structure itself and the variation upstream from this point may be calculated by undertaking a 'backwater' calculation. This requires a number of steps that again may be found in most hydraulics texts.

The distance for which water levels are affected upstream of a structure is governed by a combination of flow depth and channel slope. A simple equation for the estimation of how far the backwater effects of a structure remain significant is given below:

$$L = 0{\cdot}7D/s$$

where L = affected distance (m)
        D = normal flow depth (m)
        s = bed slope (i.e. 1 in s)

It should be noted that when the flow is controlled by a structure containing gates or valves, then there may not be a unique stage – discharge relationship for the length of channel upstream that is within the backwater zone. Moveable gates or valves mean that a different discharge may be passed by the structure for a range of water levels, or perhaps the same water level. While this provides flexible control of the river it creates a further unknown for construction risk. Conditions may only be determined with knowledge of the structure operating procedures, structure design and site specific conditions.

In any of these situations it would be appropriate to undertake a range of hand calculations to investigate the sensitivity of any estimate to changes in site conditions.

3.2.3. Estimation of flow from the catchment: the Flood Studies Report (FSR) and Flood Estimation Handbook (FEH) methods

Procedures outlined in the *Flood Studies Report* (FSR) allow flood flows to be estimated for any location. Ideally this is based on the analysis of flood peak data. However, where necessary, the FSR procedures allow estimates to be made from information derived from 1:25 000 OS maps, and certain standard charts and data given in the report.

The original FSR technique (NERC, 1975) was subsequently accepted as a standard within the industry. The calculations can be undertaken by hand or through PC software. The output from an FSR analysis typically takes the form of potential flood hydrographs associated with a design storm of given rarity (i.e. 10-year, 50-year, 100-year event, etc.). The hydrograph can be calculated for an entire catchment or the process used to estimate runoff from 'subcatchments' that can then be fed discretely into a numerical model of the river system.

The FSR has now been superseded by the *Flood Estimation Handbook* (FEH). This presents new general statistical procedures for rainfall and flood frequency estimation (Institute of Hydrology, 2000). In addition, volume 4 restates, and partially updates, the FSR rainfall-runoff method. An overview volume gives general guidance in flood estimation, including the particular task of flood-risk mapping. Digital catchment data can be viewed and extracted on a PC using the FEH CD-ROM, avoiding the need for manual abstraction of data from maps and charts. Software is also available to support the new methods of rainfall and flood-frequency estimation. The recommendation remains to base flood-frequency estimates on the flood-peak data (e.g. by annual-maximum analysis) and flood-event data (i.e. rainfall-runoff analysis), wherever possible. Details of the FEH may be obtained from CEH Wallingford (formerly the Institute of Hydrology).

3.2.4. Numerical river modelling

Where a more reliable estimate of conditions is required, or the behaviour of the river is sufficiently complex that hand calculations are difficult and unreliable, it may be more appropriate to use a numerical model to predict conditions at the site. If the proposed works are likely to have a significant, albeit transient, impact on river behaviour, the regulatory authority may also request that modelling work is undertaken to prove that such impacts are manageable and appropriate mitigation measures are being taken.

A variety of different models are available, details of which may be found in the Environment Agency benchmarking study *Benchmarking and scoping study of hydraulic river models* (Environment Agency, 1997b).

Running a model
Once a model has been built and calibrated it may be used to predict conditions for a range of flood and/or construction scenarios. Benefits include the prediction of:

- flow and water level at chosen locations for selected storm events (such as MAF, 10-year, 50-year, 100-year storm)
- section-averaged flow velocities (scale-up for local effects)
- typical duration for flood events
- typical times for catchment response to storm events
- impact of tide and tidal surge at the site
- water depths for shipping access to the site
- impact of river-structure operation at the site
- impact on river water-levels of construction works in the river.

When considering the use of a model the following should be noted:

- a model can only be as accurate and reliable as the data used to build it
- a model should be used as a tool to *aid* design, planning and engineering judgement
- the potential cost of collecting data for model construction should not be underestimated
- observed data should be used to calibrate a model whenever possible.

3.3. TIDAL EFFECTS

In estuaries and tidal reaches of rivers, tidal effects can significantly affect a construction project, both in terms of works design and works schedule (see Boxes 3.1 and 3.2). Impacts may include:

- restricted access to the site (for delivery, placing or removal of material by barge)
- restricted access limiting safety procedures
- design of temporary works to withstand tidal variations
- drainage of works to suit tidal range
- scheduling of works programme (i.e. excavation, concrete)
- changing river currents (i.e. impact on diver and plant operation)
- changing sediment patterns (i.e. likely to be fine muds).

The greatest impact for the project is likely to be for the scheduled works, whereby work below high water-level can only be undertaken during low tide periods. This means that shift working may be appropriate and that work needs to be scheduled into acceptable packages for completion between tides.

While contractors will routinely plan their operations using predicted tidal levels (high *and* low water), they need to take account of possible deviations

Box 3.1.   Welmore Sluice — Design of temporary works

The reconstruction of Welmore Lake Sluice at the tidally influenced confluence of the Delph and Hundred Foot Rivers is a good example of the way in which the consideration of temporary works and 'buildability' at the beginning of the design process can reduce construction risks. The location of the outfall was chosen not only to minimise future erosion and siltation problems, but also to allow the whole of the new structure to be built inside a 46 m diameter circular-cofferdam. This allowed a much-improved working space compared with a traditional rectangular cofferdam. Two ring beams provided the support to the sheet piling and the absence of cross bracing simplified the construction of slabs and walls in the concrete structure. The design proceeded on the assumption that the successful contractor would adopt the temporary works proposed. Although a 46 m diameter cofferdam was outside any previous experience in the UK, the method statement of all the tenderers agreed with this concept.

(Photograph courtesy of Lewin, Fryer & Partners)

(Sketch courtesy of J. Rapley and Lewin, Fryer & Partners)

Box 3.2.   A12/M11 link road — River Lea crossing

This crossing entailed the construction of bridge piers within the river channel and a realignment of part of the channel. Tidal conditions exist at the site with water levels varying from a minimum depth of 1 m at low water to a high depth of 3 m at high tide, and 5·8 m during a combined high tide/fluvial event. The River Lea also joins the River Thames upstream of the Thames Barrier, hence water levels at the site could also be affected by operation of the barrier.

Careful consideration was required when designing the cofferdams and working practice to deal with the variation in water level and to minimise impact on the river. The following steps were taken.

- An analysis of flow data from the nearest gauging station.
- The size and location of cofferdams in relation to river alignment, potential blockage and scour was considered.
- The height of the cofferdam was designed such that it remained dry for normal tidal events but could be overtopped during flood events and hence minimise blockage to the river.
- Pile design consideration: for example, under extreme conditions when water levels were high there would be no personnel working within the cofferdam and hence reduced safety factors could be applied.
- Dewatering of the cofferdam was only undertaken after any suspended sediment within the water had been allowed to settle. Dewatering was typically undertaken at the start of the day only, allowing the sediment to settle throughout the night thereby avoiding the need to use settling tanks before discharging water back into the river. Note, however, that this method could only be used with well-sealed cofferdams.

View from downstream

Box 3.2.   continued

Looking downstream along right bank (photographs courtesy of HR Wallingford/Sir Robert McAlpine)

from the predictions arising from storm surge and other effects. While considering ways in which tidal effects may be estimated, more obvious and simple factors such as the operation and impact of flood defences and tidal barriers should not be overlooked.

One way in which tidal uncertainty may be quantified and taken into account in the schedule risk modelling described in Chapter 2 is illustrated in Box 3.3.

3.3.1. Tidal behaviour

While the basic tidal cycle in an estuary can be predicted with relative ease, and tables are readily available indicating the average size and timing of the tide for any given area, there are a number of factors that contribute to tidal events which are not so easy to predict. Allowance can be made for average tidal conditions, but the level of potential variation around these conditions should also be established. In terms of water level, tidal behaviour for an estuary will depend upon:

Box 3.3. An example of evaluating the effect on programme of critical low-level operations (tidal working)

This example explores risk assessment techniques for a project which depends on working at low-tide levels. Data analysis of predicted and measured tide levels for a typical UK site (a 'standard port' has been carried out to assess the likelihood of predicted 'tide windows' not occurring due to surge effects) and the impact of not being able to carry out work as planned is illustrated using a schedule risk model. The example, therefore, combines statistical analysis of hydraulic conditions with schedule risk modelling. Other aspects could be studied in a similar way, such as the impact of high wave-heights in the construction programme.

The issues that have been explored are:

(*a*) Exposure probability. How likely is it that a tide window will be missed due to surge effects? More precisely, what is the probability that the low water-level will not fall to below a given threshold, given that it was predicted to do so?

(*b*) Exposure duration. How likely is it that the length of time a given threshold level is exposed will be significantly less than predicted? These results were used to explore the impact of missing a tidal window opportunity on an overall project schedule.

Probability of exposure of a given level
Table 3.1 illustrates the difference between measured and predicted low water-levels at the site, for a range of threshold levels.

Table 3.1.   Tidal analysis showing probability of not achieving tidal window

Number of low waters			6886
Threshold level: m ODN	Predicted no. of low waters below threshold	Predicted proportion of tides below threshold: %	Probability that measured tide level is above threshold: %
0	6886	100·0	0·0
−1	6691	97·2	1·4
−1·5	5780	83·9	3·3
−1·8	4862	70·6	4·1
−2·2	3452	50·1	7·7
−2·5	2187	31·8	11·2
−2·7	1386	20·1	12·8
−2·9	797	11·6	15·9
−3	554	8·0	17·0
−3·1	381	5·5	17·3
−3·3	170	2·5	21·2
−3·5	59	0·86	30·5
−3·6	30	0·44	43·3
−3·7	14	0·20	64·3
−3·9	1	0·015	
−4	0	0·000	

Box 3.3. continued

The total number of low waters in the record is 6886. The first column shows the threshold level, i.e. the low water-level below which work can proceed. The second and third columns show the number and proportion of predicted low waters that fall below the threshold. These do not include the effect of surge, and are obtained from predicted tide curves. For lower threshold levels, the proportion of predicted tides that expose the threshold level decreases progressively.

It therefore becomes increasingly important not to miss a tide window, since the time to wait until the next one may significantly affect the construction programme.

The fourth column shows the probability that the observed water level fails to expose the threshold level, *given that it was predicted to do so*. In terms of a particular construction operation which requires a given level to be exposed, this represents a failure. The likelihood of failure is due to the difference between observed and predicted water levels as a result of meteorological effects which cannot be predicted long in advance.

The likelihood of failure increases as the threshold level (i.e. working level) decreases. This implies that the more rare the predicted tide window, the more likely it is that work will not be able to be carried out as planned. This may have a serious impact on the construction programme, particularly as there may be a long time to wait for the next opportunity to carry out the work.

The main reason for the increasing likelihood of missing a tidal window is that at low levels, the surge component has a greater influence, relative to the difference between the threshold level and the predicted tide level. There may also be other, site specific, factors such as the dependence between tide level and surge.

Exposure duration
The main aim of this analysis is to show the risk of having insufficient working time at a working level which is exposed at low water. This is important for operations such as preparing foundations and inspection, and is a major factor in the decision to use land-based plant. In some cases the operation may be critical to the programme, in which case a missed opportunity to work due to surge effects may have a disproportionate effect on the overall programme. The likelihood of exposure duration being less than expected, and the potential impact on a project, was explored based on the same data sets as the level probability analysis just described. The results are given in Table 3.2.

Of the tides predicted to expose the working level for sufficient duration, a proportion in fact fail to do so due to surge effects. The fourth column shows the proportion of observed tides which fail to expose the working level for the required duration, even though they were predicted to do so.

Assuming that the work is planned to match the predicted time available, the analysis confirms that the longer the duration required for the work, the less likely it becomes that sufficient time will be available.

Use of tidal data in schedule risk assessment
The analysis of exposure duration was incorporated into a project-schedule model to illustrate the impact of missing a tidal window on the finish date of a project.

In the project envisaged, it was assumed that the contractor would need to take advantage of low waters over the spring-tide periods to carry out preparatory work on the river bed. As this work was to be carried out by land-based plant, the water level had to expose the river bed at the working level for sufficient duration to carry out the work.

Box 3.3.   continued

It was assumed that a duration of least 2·5 hours would be required to mobilise plant and carry out work, and it was estimated that the preparatory work could be completed during two (non consecutive) low-water periods, provided both met the 2·5 hour exposure criterion. The working level selected was −2·15 m ODN. The likelihood and impact of delays due to tidal working was then predicted by the method of schedule risk analysis. The completion date, assuming that all tidal work is carried out as planned, would have been about 24 February 1996. However, the impact of any missed tidal window has a knock-on effect to the end of the project so there was a probability of completion on this date of only 73%. The probability of completion two weeks later was about 22%, and four weeks late, about 4%. There was a small chance (about 1%) that the project would have to be extended to six or more weeks behind schedule.

It should be borne in mind that in this analysis, there were no subsequent operations requiring a low-level tidal window. If such operations existed the total project delay would have exceeded the figures quoted.

Table 3.2.   Duration criteria for tidal working

Duration criteria

Threshold duration: hours	No. of predicted tides greater than threshold	Proportion of tides greater than threshold: %	Likelihood of not being able to work as planned: %
Working level = − 1·3 (MLWN)			
1	6091	88·5	3·20
1·5	5911	85·8	3·38
2	5641	81·9	4·19
2·5	5132	74·5	6·10
3	4288	62·3	9·81
3·5	2719	39·5	15·3
4	858	12·5	22·4
4·5	71	1·0	35·2
5	0	0·0	
Working level = − 2·15 (MLWN+MLWS)/2			
1	3193	46·4	9·27
1·5	2585	37·5	11·8
2	1743	25·3	14·9
2·5	831	12·1	21·5
3	223	3·2	24·7
3·5	11	0·2	45·5
4	0	0·0	
Working level = − 3·00 (MLWS)			
0·5	402	5·8	17·2
1	269	3·9	20·0
1·5	132	1·9	29·5
2	21	0·3	28·6
2·5	0	0·0	

Box 3.3. continued

Comment

This type of analysis demonstrates the use of statistical analysis of hydraulic data allied to activity network software to evaluate the schedule risk profile of a project.

However, the example is 'static' in that there is no feedback between the delay and the resources. In most real projects there would be an increase in resources in the event of a slippage in an attempt to make up time. In this case that might take the form of increasing the amount of plant devoted to the preparatory work in order to minimise the likelihood of further delay.

- astronomical tide

plus

- storm surges
- wind set-up
- wave set-up
- seiches
- river discharge.

Meteorological and seismic effects (seiches) are not predictable more than, at best, a few days in advance (seiches only a few hours!), and even then the predictions are very uncertain. It is these aspects that can pose a risk to the construction works.

3.3.2. Estimating tidal site conditions

For construction works the wind, wave, water level and current data may be presented in two forms:

- normal conditions or climate (i.e. statistical presentation of the data showing a range of conditions which can be used for planning purposes)
- extreme conditions (i.e. statistical maximum conditions which can be used for planning and design of temporary works).

It is worth noting that the following generic references may contain information relating to conditions at the site of interest:

- shoreline management plans
- estuary management plans
- shoreline strategy studies.

Data requirement and manipulation

In order to predict conditions at a site it is necessary to collate information on wind, wave and water levels. There are many different sources of data and techniques for manipulating and transforming data to the site of interest. For example, wave data are often available from offshore sites but to be applicable to an estuary location the data must be processed to simulate wave travel into the shallow water of the estuary. Alternatively, in the absence of recorded wave data, potential wave heights can be estimated theoretically using fetch lengths. Tables A8.1 to A8.5 in Appendix 8 provide a summary of potential data sources and techniques for their manipulation. A more detailed description of these techniques may be found in *Construction risk in coastal engineering* (Simm and Cruickshank, 1998).

Estimation of extreme water levels
Extreme water levels may be obtained from published extreme water levels (e.g. POL, 1997) at numerous locations and converted to the site of interest. Any uncertainty involved in calculating extreme water levels in this way is usually small compared to uncertainties associated with prediction of extreme wave conditions and to an assessment of their correlation with extreme water levels. An approximate method for deriving extreme water levels based on published extreme values for another nearby location is given in Box 3.4.

It should be noted that this technique provides extreme conditions assuming no influence from river flow. This technique is not appropriate when calculating tidal levels combined with significant river flows.

3.3.3. Predicting wave size and force

Where the construction site may be subject to wave action, the forces that these waves may apply to structures should be considered during both temporary and permanent works design. It should be noted that significant sized waves may be generated along straight stretches of river, lakes or reservoirs, far inland from the coastal area and their errosive effects can be significant in relation to currents.

Prediction of wave height
Wave heights may be predicted using fetch length and area, wind speed, duration, etc. Similar techniques may be applied to the estimation of waves from the open

---

Box 3.4. Simple approach to correlating extreme water levels (CIRIA, 1996b)

One way of deriving a first estimate of a probability distribution of extreme water levels for a site for which there is only basic astronomical tidal information is to correlate this site with one nearby for which both tidal data and extreme water level predictions are available. Correlation is then achieved by assuming (Graff, 1981) that the following ratio is the same for the two sites:

$$\frac{\text{Extreme level} - \text{mean high water spring (MHWS) level}}{\text{Spring tide range (MHWS} - \text{MLWS)}}$$

Where available and appropriate, a slightly more accurate estimate can be achieved by replacing spring tidal range in the above ratio by the sum of the principal semi-diurnal tidal components (CIRIA, 1996b).

---

sea, on reservoirs and in rivers. The HR Wallingford report *Reservoir dams: wave conditions, wave overtopping and slab protection* (HR Wallingford, 1996b) outlines techniques applied to wave prediction in reservoirs and for run-up/ overtopping of revetments.

Prediction of wave force

Wave forces on structures may be estimated using a variety of techniques. An important distinction is whether or not the waves are breaking on a structure. Waves that are breaking exert a considerably greater force than those that are not, and the calculation procedure therefore differs.

Forces from pulsating or non-breaking waves may be calculated using the Goda formula (Goda, 1985). Applying this technique to the design of sheet piled cofferdams is mentioned in CIRIA (1993) where BS 6349: Part 1 is referred to.

Wave impact forces may be predicted using methods described in HR Wallingford reports *Wave forces on vertical and composite breakwaters* (HR Wallingford, 1996a) and in *Forces on vertical breakwaters: effects of oblique or short vertical waves* (HR Wallingford, 1999a). Additional information was produced by the EU PROVERBS (Probabilistic Design Tools for Vertical Breakwaters) research project.

Note that guidance on the use of rock for protection against wave action may also be found in CIRIA (1991).

3.3.4. Tidal currents

Tidal effects can alter significantly the way in which a river behaves and hence affect construction works. The most obvious tidal effect is upon river flow. As the tidal cycle progresses the river level will change and flow velocity will vary. Under some circumstances a tidal bore may occur whereby a wave will travel back up the river marking the rising tide. What may be less obvious is the nature of flow under the water surface. Since the density of water varies with salinity, salt water from the rising tide will often sit on the river bed with fresh water flowing over the surface. This may affect water temperature, quality and hence visibility, all of which could affect the actions and safety of divers.

3.3.5. Tidal limits

While 'official' tidal limits for UK rivers are shown on OS maps by the line density along the river bank, the true tidal limit may be different. If the structure at which the tidal effects are contained has gates that can be drowned or can be overtopped during high spring or surge events then tidal influence may reach further upstream. Equally, the construction and operation of a tidal defence scheme may alter significantly the way in which the river reacts to extreme tidal events. True limits and tidal impact should be confirmed by local sources.

3.4. REAL-TIME FORECASTING

Real-time forecasting may be required for operational purposes, to plan site activities on a day by day basis. The level to which this may be done will depend upon the nature of works and the construction site. Two examples are given in Boxes 3.5 and 3.6 that detail different systems, used in both the fluvial and coastal environments.

As the Internet develops in size and sophistication, there are an increasing number of sites from which real-time data (e.g. weather forecasts) may be obtained. Use of the Internet to provide raw data and flood warning information is growing. For example, systems are now active in California that allow the public to have access to real-time gauging station data along rivers such that the development and progression of a flood wave along a valley may be monitored

---

Box 3.5. Examples of the use of real-time modelling

Samphire Hoe

Samphire Hoe is an area of reclaimed land, using waste from the Channel Tunnel, which is protected by a concrete seawall. This has produced about 70 acres of land to be made available to the general public for informal recreation including walking and fishing.

Bad weather and tidal surges mean that at times the wall is vulnerable to high waves breaking over it. Client Eurotunnel commissioned HR Wallingford to recommend a hazard warning system for the seawall, and the Meteorological Office was brought in to help.

The warning system uses hour by hour predictions of the total water level around the Hoe along with wind-speed and direction converted into timings for predicted high-risk overtopping. The information is faxed twice a day from the London Weather Centre to Eurotunnel's office at Longport. If overtopping is predicted, warning flags are put out along the Hoe, or it can be evacuated if necessary. In its first year of service there were 20 red-flag alerts.

While this service was site specific to the Hoe, similar systems could be used elsewhere for warning of overtopping and flood risks. It could also assist with construction activities along the coastline by examining proposed timings and methods of work.

Box 3.6. Weir replacement on the River Lee

An old weir required removal and reconstruction. It was decided that the best option for undertaking the works was to completely dam-off the weir during removal and reconstruction, with the river flow being diverted through a temporary diversion channel. In the event of a large flood, sections of the cofferdam could be removed to allow flow to pass through the works.

Catchment response for the river at the construction site was relatively slow. In the event of a storm event in the catchment it would take two to three days for the peak discharge to occur at the site. It was therefore considered sufficient to simply monitor water levels at the site by recording levels hourly and to control levels by adjusting a weir control into the diversion channel.

---

from the desktop. Such information would be invaluable for construction planning in the UK.

3.5. SCOUR AND DEPOSITION

The potential impact of scour or deposition on the construction project should not be underestimated. Any construction works that change the way in which the river behaves (or flows) will alter the local morphology and may therefore induce scour or deposition at the site (see examples in Boxes 3.7, 3.8 and 3.9). This will need to be anticipated and allowed for in both temporary and permanent works design.

Of equal importance is the possible impact on river morphology elsewhere. If significant changes to river behaviour are induced then this may cause changes within the river morphology at other locations. For example, partially blocking the river flow may cause a subtle change in the direction of flow during flood events. This change may not be noticeable at low flows. The change in flow direction may then, for example, result in increased scour around a nearby structure, such as a railway bridge, and lead to failure of the structure. Liability for such a series of events can now be traced back to the original cause and responsibility must rest with the designer to ensure that such events do not occur.

3.5.1. Prediction of scour

There are many equations for the estimation of scour and no single definitive answer. The processes involved are not fully understood and the best approach to predicting scour is therefore through a combination of engineering judgement and analysis, using a wide range of equations. The selection of equations will depend upon both the nature of the obstruction by construction works, the type of flow, and the type of bed material present. The prediction of scour within the tidal zone uses different equations to that within unidirectional river flow.

Box 3.7. Bridge pier repair on the River Eden, Carlisle

Scour problems had been identified around a bridge pier in the River Eden at Carlisle. Protection of the pier was proposed and in order to undertake the works a cofferdam was constructed around the pier. In doing so half of the river channel was blocked, with no consideration given to the impact that this might have on local flow conditions and water levels.

Scour problems developed quite quickly along the opposite bridge abutment where all of the river flow was being diverted. Emergency repair and protection measures had to be undertaken to ensure the safety of the bridge. Work was completed around the bridge pier within the cofferdam, however, the cost of overlooking the potential impacts of changing flow conditions proved quite high!

Box 3.8. Impact of works at other sites

On the 7 February 1989 the Inverness Railway Viaduct collapsed into the River Ness. The mainline railway link through Scotland was broken for over a year and the cost of replacing the structure exceeded £2 million. The failure could be attributed to dredging works in the harbour area downstream of the bridge.

Lowering the river-bed level in the harbour area caused bed levels further upstream to lower, and the river-bed gradient to steepen. As this effect continued upstream to the bridge structure and beyond, bed levels around the bridge piers lowered until the foundations were undermined leading to failure.

(Photographs courtesy of HR Wallingford)

Box 3.9. Inadequate stream capacity/scour protection measures

An aggregate company wished to extract gravel through open-pit mining but two rivers passed directly across the proposed site. In order to minimise costs, the first river was diverted into the second, and the second subsequently around the extraction site (Figure 3.1).

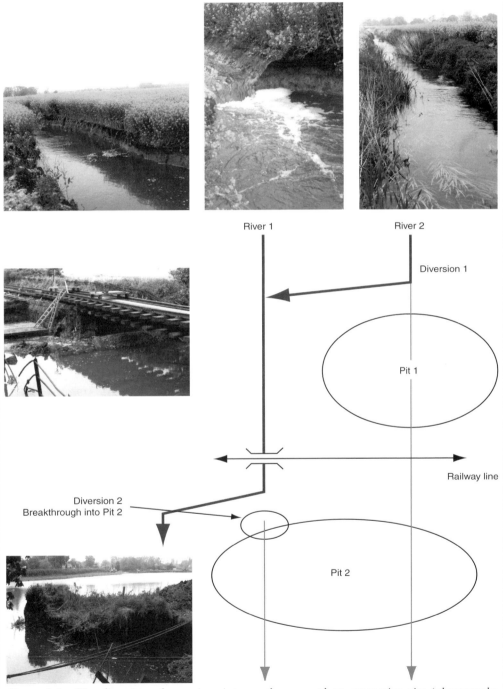

Figure 3.1. The diversion of one river into another around an excavation site (photographs courtesy of HR Wallingford)

Box 3.9. continued

No consideration was given to the flood capacity of the second channel. Although under normal flow conditions the diversion appeared reasonable (in terms of channel capacity), the channel was insufficient under flood conditions, as was the scour protection placed at the second diversion point. During a minor flood event the flow eroded through bank protection and flooded into the excavation works. Subsequently the flow eroded bed-levels back from the 'drop' into the pit, naturally widening and deepening the flow channel. This effect rapidly progressed upstream from the pit and undermined foundations at the railway bridge causing it to collapse.

A combination of inadequate scour protection and hydraulic design resulted in complete flooding of the works, destruction of the railway bridge and erosion of a large reach of river channel through farmland!

It is recommended that expert advice is sought where the reliability of a potential scour estimate poses a significant risk to the project. However, for further information on scour processes and calculation techniques for both river and tidal zones the following references are recommended. For scour in rivers, *Scouring, hydraulic structures design manual* (Breusers and Raudkivi, 1991) and for scour in tidal zones, *Scour at marine structures* (Whitehouse, 1998).

3.5.2. Scour monitoring

Where the impact of scour on the river or the construction works could lead to serious problems, whether from financial, environmental or safety perspectives, the use of scour monitors may be appropriate. A number of systems are sold commercially and may be installed at locations of specific interest. There are two basic types of system: buried sensor systems or sonic systems. Buried sensors work on the basis of installing the system into the bed material such that when the sensors are exposed (or buried) a signal is generated (or not) (see Box 3.10). Sonar systems work on the basis of projecting a beam onto the bed and measuring the returned signal and hence variation in bed level. Both systems have advantages and disadvantages. Fundamentally, buried sensors are harder to install and care is needed to ensure that any disturbed material is not prone to accelerated scour. However, once in place, the sensors generally operate more reliably than sonar systems that, on the contrary, are relatively easy to install but can suffer interference from debris and sediment, particularly during flood events when concentrations are high.

3.5.3. Movement of bed or excavated material

If excavation works are undertaken in the wet and left exposed to river or tidal flows, it is likely that movement of sediment will occur. In addition to the potential for pollution, this can have the effect of both moving and dispersing any excavated material placed on the bed and infilling, or slumping of the excavation.

Box 3.10. Application of scour monitors

Scour monitors were initially developed to identify and predict scour at structures such as bridges. They may be applied, however, to any situation where scour or accretion of sediment needs to be monitored.

Shingle beach movement — Shoreham
A line of 'stand alone' monitors were installed down the beach to monitor changes in the beach profile.

Stand alone monitor system (left) — sensors mounted on stem with data logger in head unit and (right) single scour sensor (photographs courtesy of HR Wallingford)

Scour protection for the Rotherhithe Tunnel, River Thames
Following concern that the Rotherhithe Tunnel would be exposed to the river by scour and bed movement, works were undertaken to protect the bed over and around the tunnel using layered stone protection. To ensure that the protection was, and remained, effective scour monitors were installed within the protection layers to form a permanent monitoring system.

Careful analysis of local flow conditions and sediment type is required if the potential impact on and of the flow is to be assessed. Since any such assessment cannot be precise and will rely on engineering skill and judgement, a balance needs to be made between excavation size and duration and the magnitude of any effects. The larger and longer the excavation, the more efficient it is likely to be for the project; a larger and longer excavation will however increase the risk of sediment effects (see Boxes 3.11 and 3.12).

Box 3.11.   Pipeline crossing of the River Lochy at Fort William

It was necessary to lay a new sewage pipeline across the River Lochy near Fort William. The river is a gravel-bed river subject to flash flooding, tidal influence and hence changes in bed profile. It also offers a prime site for salmon fishing.

Construction of the pipeline needed to consider the following issues:

- Gravel bed rivers naturally armour the bed through erosion of fine material. Excavation would disturb this armouring effect. Backfilling would need to consider this.
- Bed material could be eroded easily with local disruption of flow.
- Any excavated channel would backfill relatively quickly.
- Release of fine sediments in the river would disturb salmon.
- Plant would need to negotiate both deep and shallow river sections.

Actual construction was successfully completed by:

- Excavating and laying the pipeline in two halves. This minimised the duration of exposure for the excavation to flow and made handling of the shorter pipeline lengths easier. It did create the secondary problem of connecting the two pipeline halves, which had to be undertaken by divers.
- The excavation was protected by a rip-rap layer, rather than simply backfilling with excavated material. Excess material was used as landscaping along the banks (with care required to ensure no worsening of flood conditions).
- A bund was constructed across the shallow half of the river for access. The crest level was set at mean high-tide level such that it would be overtopped during a flood event, so minimising the increase in potential flood levels. Excavation was undertaken immediately downstream of the bund within the flooded, but protected, area.

(Photograph courtesy of HR Wallingford)

Box 3.11.   continued

- Rip-rap material was temporarily placed upstream of the bund to create a protected lagoon. Excavated material could be safely stored in the lagoon which minimised the release of sediments, prevented movement of the material and minimised travel time for excavation plant.
- Excavation through the deeper section of river was undertaken using plant from a floating pontoon.

Box 3.12.   Reconstruction of Inverness Railway Viaduct

Following failure of the original viaduct a replacement structure was built. This entailed clearance of old debris, construction of a new weir to maintain a minimum bed level and construction of the new bridge. As a result of the earlier collapse a large, deep longitudinal channel had been cut between bridge pier locations that caued a concentration in flow. Prior to construction of the bridge it was decided that this should be infilled to redistribute flow more evenly across the channel.

Initial filling was undertaken by pushing material into the hole from one bank. This was soon stopped as it was quickly discovered that as the hole was infilled from one bank, more material was eroded from the other side. This simply had the effect of moving the scour channel laterally across the channel, and indeed towards some existing bridge piers. The only solution was to infill the hole evenly. This entailed the placing of material directly into the hole from above — a considerably more complex and costly exercise!

(Photograph courtesy of HR Wallingford)

3.6. DEBRIS

Debris can create a number of problems during a construction project. Debris may arrive at a site courtesy of the river, it may be generated on site or it may already be buried within an excavation area. Possible threats to a project may include:

- accumulation and blockage of flow causing flooding
- accumulation around structures causing scour
- impact and accumulated loading on structures
- buried debris causing obstruction to excavation or piling works
- cost of continued removal of debris.

Boxes 3.13, 3.14 and 3.15 highlight some of the construction problems associated with debris.

3.6.1. Booms and trash racks

If river flow is being diverted or deflected around construction works and there is a serious risk of blockage from debris, it may be appropriate to install a boom or rack upstream of the site to collect debris before it can cause any problems. Care needs to be taken in the design and positioning of such systems however, since an over designed rack will efficiently collect all debris and is likely to

---

Box 3.13. Obstructions to pile driving

A common problem when working with piles close to existing structures is to encounter foundation stones and/or debris within the river bed that obstruct clear driving of the piles. The true extent of foundation works for older structures is often not known. Adequate site investigation prior to construction is the only reliable way of determining the extent and nature of any potential blockage.

The boulders (right) were removed from the bed when pile driving was required for works to the bridge arch (photographs courtesy of Mott MacDonald)

Box 3.14. Gainsborough flood alleviation scheme

The works provide a high quality rigid flood defence with a new public walkway over a length of approximately 800 m. Construction has been phased to ensure that the present defences will be replaced first at the end of their useful lives, as well as giving consideration to access and adjacent properties. The working environment is tidal with a high tidal-range and varying ground conditions, resulting in an ever-changing environment. As the proposed works would reduce the river width by 5–6 m, a mathematical model was used to determine the effect on river hydraulics, which subsequently determined that the effect of increasing river levels and velocities was negligible.

Three major considerations were identified at the feasibility stage that have dramatically affected the design and construction, namely:

- To ensure that future maintenance of the full length of the new works could be undertaken in an economically and safe manner, sufficient access would be required.
- The new works should not rely on the existing frontage defences for any part of their stability.
- Any further development of the already narrow sites should not be prejudiced and the existing buildings not endangered in any manner.

Piling close to waterfront buildings was delayed by the need to remove tree stumps that had been cut off near bed level (photographs courtesy of S. Kent, Environment Agency)

quickly become clogged. This may create a risk of flooding that is worse than the original problem! Boxes 3.16, 3.17 and 3.18 give examples of trash collection systems and highlight typical trash-related problems.

3.6.2. Debris impact

Large debris in the river, such as tree trunks, combined with high river-flow velocities, may provide the debris with sufficient momentum to cause damage to temporary works, should a direct hit occur. Guidance on the design of sheet piled cofferdams (CIRIA, 1993) recommends allowing for debris 'where appropriate'.

Box 3.15. Reconstruction of Bray Weir on the River Thames

Construction work at Bray Weir was delayed significantly, with later phases of work shifted to the following summer, owing to the discovery of an extensive mesh of timbers below the existing structure. The timbers were so extensive that it proved easier to modify the new structure foundation design than to cut and remove them from the mud. Located beneath the existing weir, these timbers were only discovered following demolition of the existing superstructure and could not easily have been detected prior to the works. Following the project it was concluded that *serious consideration* should be given to the risk of encountering hidden structures in similar situations and that the option of relocation of any new structures away from existing structure should be considered carefully (Higgs *et al*, 1998).

Box 3.16. Woolston Guard Weir

While this case study reflects a design risk, the problem applies equally to temporary works design and hence construction risk.

A new weir was constructed across the River Mersey near Warrington which incorporated nine air-regulated siphon bays. During flood conditions the River Mersey passes a considerable amount, and range, of debris. To reduce the risk of blockage within the siphons a trash rack was constructed across a 'guard weir' that was located 200 m upstream from the new weir. The trash rack comprised single vertical bars at 300 mm spacing that extended down to approximately two thirds of the river depth.

(Photograph courtesy of HR Wallingford)

Box 3.16. continued

The trash rack was so effective at collecting debris that the Manchester Ship Canal Company was forced to spend considerable sums of money clearing the rack and removing debris on a weekly basis. Eventually, during a flood, the amount of debris collected was so large that it blocked the rack over its full depth. Debris then began to pass under the rack. Combined with the debris 'released' from the rack during attempts to clear the blockage, this proceeded downstream to the new weir site where it was observed to pass safely through the siphon structure! Subsequent removal of the trash rack has not led to any difficulties with debris at the new weir.

In this instance it transpired that debris was not really a problem after all. Constructing a trash rack was considered preferable to accepting the unknown risk of blockage of the new weir. Unique to this location, controls on the Manchester Ship Canal offered an alternative means for coping with the conditions created by blockage of the trash rack. The ability to divert flood flow along the Ship Canal meant that this risk could be accepted on a temporary basis in order to assess the true conditions and required solution.

Box 3.17. Typical debris removed from Woolston Old Weir on the River Mersey

(Photograph courtesy of HR Wallingford)

The potential force on a structure may be calculated by assuming a design debris load, velocity of flow and potential time and deflection upon impact. When considering debris impact for the design of bridge structures (Farraday *et al.*, 1983), the Australian Specification suggests the use of a 2 tonne log travelling at stream velocity and stopped in a deflection distance of 150 mm or 75 mm for columns and solid type piers. Practice within some UK consultants is to use a 10 tonne log stopped within a deflection distance of 75 mm.

The pressure caused by trapped debris may also create an appreciable load. Again considering bridge design specifications, it is common to adopt conditions

Box 3.18.   Dealing with debris

Shopping trolleys are commonly found in rivers near to developed areas

Trash boom being installed at a new weir (photographs courtesy of HR Wallingford)

for potential pier loading, such as a width of debris built up to equal half the sum of the two span widths around the pier, with debris accumulated to a minimum depth of 1·2 m.

3.7. WORKS LOCATION

The location, or choice of location for the works in relation to the river, will directly affect the types and level of construction risk for the project. A balance must be made between construction advantages and the associated risks.

3.7.1. Access

Access to a site, whether permanent or temporary, may be affected by many factors.

By land:

- access route subject to flooding/poor ground conditions
- route subject to tides/waves
- limited space
- route through an environmentally sensitive area
- route through an urban area — traffic, noise, mud, dust, etc.

By water:

- river flow conditions — water level too high or too low, local currents
- wave conditions
- navigation constraints, e.g. public events such as regattas.

To cope with such variations in conditions the following measures may be required:

- flood and weather warning systems
- temporary road construction
- temporary removal/demolition of existing structures — planning permission required
- constraints on work programme — traffic frequency, hours, noise, pollution, etc.

Boxes 3.19 and 3.20 highlight two examples of access problems for construction projects.

Box 3.19. New weir, central Oxford

Refurbishment of an old weir in central Oxford was constrained by very limited working space. Use of road space alongside the site was not permissible.

The contractor solved both the problem of access and of working space by constructing a temporary platform across the site from which plant could both work and access all areas. At the start of construction, however, the project was delayed by one week since the proposed method of working entailed demolition of a short section of wall for which planning permission had been overlooked!

(Photograph courtesy of HR Wallingford/Environment Agency)

Box 3.20. Channel Tunnel

During construction of the Channel Tunnel, monitoring of coastal waters was undertaken either side of the reclamation site at the foot of Shakespeare Cliff in order to ensure that sediments placed within the reclamation area were not 'leaking' from the site. While the monitoring sites were stationed at the foot of the cliffs above the high water level, access was via a road along the top of the beach. At high tide this road was not flooded but suffered frequent overtopping by large waves. Accordingly, access to and from the site was restricted to periods other than near high tide.

3.7.2. River diversion

In some situations it may prove more cost effective to divert the river to allow construction of the works. River diversions take many forms and can be undertaken in many ways (see Boxes 3.21, 3.22 and 3.23):

Timescale:	Temporary or permanent
Nature:	Partial or complete
Closure:	Embankment, sheet piling, new structure, portadam
Diversion:	Pumped, gravity pipework, temporary channel, new river channel, ponded (alternative route)

A permanent diversion will be required to offer the same performance under flood conditions as the existing channel. It is unlikely that a worsening of flood water levels would be permissible. When considering a temporary diversion, however, the issue of what is an appropriate level of flood protection arises. The design of any diversion system should be related to the size and frequency of flood for the river at the construction site and the nature and duration of the construction project. A consistent level of risk should be aimed for. It would be excessive to construct a dam that could withstand a 100-year flood, if the diversion was required for only one day. Equally, a system that is not sufficiently reliable or safe may fail or be overtopped frequently during the construction works, leading to additional costs on the project and posing a threat to life.

Where possible, design of the diversion system, and works in the original channel, should be arranged so that if the diversion system fails or is overtopped, the excess flow can return along the original channel in preference to flooding the area.

A method for assessing appropriate levels of risk in design is outlined in Section 2.7 of Chapter 2. The design of a river diversion will need to consider:

- structural performance when overtopped
- potential for scour — around the dam, in the diversion channel at the downstream discharge point
- reliability of the system — implications of failure for the works and worker safety
- environmental impacts.

There are also a number of potential environmental impacts that should be considered, including:

- changes to river behaviour — flow and levels
- release of sediments
- impact/restriction on fish movement
- impact on local flora/fauna.

Detailed guidance on the design, construction and operation of river diversion schemes may be found in an HR Wallingford project report (for DETR) on river diversions (HR Wallingford, 1999b).

3.7.3. Flood risk

The location of works will affect and be affected by potential flooding from the river. Potential flood impact on the works will need to be minimised to reduce exposure to flood-related delay or costs. Allowable impact of the works on the river will be dictated by the relevant regulatory authority. Where the construction

---

Box 3.21.   West Drayton, Phase III — Thorney Weir

An existing structure — Thorney Weir — was to be removed and a new weir constructed. It was thought initially that the new weir would be constructed in two halves, with partial blockage of the river, but the contractor subsequently identified that cutting a temporary diversion channel for the river and building the new weir as a single unit was more cost effective.

A diversion channel 2·5 m wide was constructed and protected against scour through a combination of sheet piling and stone filled gabions. Flow through the channel was controlled by a temporary sluice structure with upstream river levels monitored by gauge boards.

View from upstream. River diverted by a temporary earth bund into the diversion channel on the right-hand side. Access for crane via the temporary bridge over the channel

---

Box 3.21. continued

Inlet to diversion channel — flow controlled by boards as required

Outflow from diversion channel into downstream channel

Both the river and weir sites were 'environmentally sensitive' with key issues including noise, flow disturbance to river, sediments, site access, pollution and fish.

Following successful bunding of the old weir, fish were removed from the enclosed pond and released into the river downstream (Photographs courtesy of HR Wallingford/Environment Agency)

Box 3.22.   Lower Colne improvement scheme — Lino Mill

During redevelopment of the Lino Mill site for industrial use, the opportunity was taken to enhance a length of the river channel and to replace (and move) a sluice structure. As space was limited the river flow was routed through the construction site using a PortaDam and piping.

PortaDam with entrance to pipe running through the site

Looking downstream along the modified line of the river channel

Box 3.22. continued

Risks in using this technique of flow diversion include:

- potential overtopping and failure of the PortaDam
- risk of puncturing dam or pipe during routine works
- risk of failure of joints between lengths of piping
- susceptibility to vandalism
- risk of drowning if sucked into the pipe.

Downstream discharge point for pipework (note environmental stonework features to enhance habitat) (Photographs courtesy of HR Wallingford/Environment Agency)

Box 3.23. Reconstruction of Bray Weir on the River Thames

This project did not include diversion of the river, but there were contractual arrangements to remove part of the cofferdam in the event of a significant flood. This would then allow flood water to pass through the works in order to reduce the adverse impact on flooding caused by the cofferdam itself. During construction a flood event did occur that required just such action. Given the geomorphological nature of the Thames catchment, the contractor was forewarned of the likelihood of flooding and was able to remove plant and equipment from the cofferdam in advance. Subsequently, 1 in 3 piles were removed from the cofferdam structure, a task that took several hours. Final flood damage to the works was minimal, and in preference to worse flooding of the local area. Divers were required to facilitate reconstruction of the cofferdam and then works continued as before.

works potentially have a large impact on flood water levels, it may be appropriate to undertake temporary mitigation measures. For example, a large site on the floodplain may be protected from flooding (to a specified level), through the construction of flood banks around the site. To compensate for the loss of floodplain storage however, additional flood storage may be created through excavation of a reservoir area that could be drained after the flood event. Care is required when considering such possibilities since any compensatory storage will need to operate at the same stage of a flood event as the original flood plain storage.

3.7.4. Groundwater

Construction adjacent to a river is likely to encounter groundwater levels closely related to the river water level (see Boxes 3.24 and 3.25). This can create a number of problems when trying to dewater the construction works:

- Potential impact of dewatering on local river levels — too much pumping adjacent to a small river or stream may be sufficient to dry out the stream.
- Dewatering may not be feasible if ground material is too permeable (e.g. running sand) and river flow is relatively high.
- Flood variations in the local river may have a significant effect on groundwater levels even if the floodplain is not inundated.

3.7.5. Ground conditions

Since the geology of river valleys is often dominated by weak alluvial materials, high groundwater levels and, also, because the river course will have moved in its geological past, ground conditions are often problematical in river and estuary engineering projects. The risks will impact on:

- stability of foundations
- stability of excavations, cofferdams and retaining walls
- ground heave
- slope stability of the permanent and temporary works
- assumptions of active and passive pressures and compressibility
- flotation, at all stages of construction.

The design of both permanent and temporary works must therefore properly consider the following:

- Ground investigations should be extensive and certainly more than would normally be expected in sites away from river valleys. Some engineers may feel that there is a percentage of the value of the works (e.g. 5%), which could justifiably be spent on ground investigations. However, this ignores the

Box 3.24. Dewatering adjacent to the River Mersey

It was proposed to construct a new weir and permanent channel across an existing river meander (see illustrations below). In this way the structure could be constructed in the dry and the river flow diverted upon completion. Construction of the structure, however, required excavation below the local groundwater level for a prolonged period of time. River water levels were affected by a combination of fluvial flow, control structures and tidal conditions (extreme tides and surges).

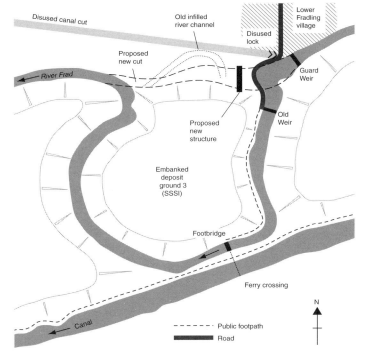

Figure 3.2. New channel and structure to bypass existing river meander

Trial pumping to develop and test drainage system

Box 3.24.   continued

Excavation of new river channel

Pumping system used during construction (middle and bottom picture)

Box 3.24.   continued

Successful control of water level at the site during construction was undertaken by combining a number of techniques. These were:

- lowering of local river water levels by altering operational procedures at weir and sluice controls
- local drawdown of the groundwater through an extensive system of well points and pumps
- construction of a flood embankment to prevent tidal surge flooding of the site
- monitoring of flow and water level from the upstream catchment.

Construction of the syphon weir (downstream channel flooded)

Finished weir in operation (photographs courtesy of HR Wallingford)

Box 3.25. Refurbishment of penstocks — central Oxford

A set of penstocks controlled the abstraction of water out of the River Thames into a stream running parallel to the river. The two channels were divided by a bank approximately 4 m wide which was protected by stonework. The penstocks were simply set in the centre of a cut through the bank, set normal to the direction of flow.

The project required the complete removal and replacement of the penstocks. This was undertaken by driving a 'box' of sheet piles around both upstream and downstream faces to create a cofferdam, and then pumping out the trapped water. In the event, the water level within the dam could not be lowered to a suitable working level, although the sheet piling was working well, because the embankment and stonework into which the piling connected were very old and porous. This allowed a significant flow to pass through the stonework, the embankment and into the works.

The work was eventually completed through a combination of grouting and increased pumping.

(Photograph courtesy of HR Wallingford/Environment Agency)

principles of risk management, as the extent of ground investigations must be dependent on the risks associated with the particular work and the consequences should they occur. This is often largely independent of the value of the works themselves. The extent of the investigations carried out at initial feasibility stage and again where required at the detailed design stage is one of the most important risk management decisions taken in the development stages of a project.

- The monitoring of groundwater levels requires a proper understanding of the water pressures actually being measured, in which strata they occur and how this will impact on soil strengths and imposed loading. Groundwater levels tend to be more variable in the vicinity of rivers and estuaries.
- Designers must fully understand the significance of long and short-term soil strengths and the role of effective and total stress analyses.

- Any ground investigation will only sample a small percentage of the total volume of the strata influencing the works. The sensitivity of the design of both permanent and temporary works to possible variations in the underlying strata should be fully investigated.

3.8. NAVIGATION

If the river or estuary is of navigable depth, then the potential effects both on and from navigation, should be considered.

If the works cause significant disruption to navigation, then there may also be adverse effects on the flow behaviour that could affect traditional navigation of the area. Combined with shipping being unfamiliar with the modified navigation route, there is likely to be an increased chance of mistakes and of possible ship impacts. While designing temporary works to withstand ship impact is unlikely to be realistic, alternative measures such as warning signs and piling to deflect craft, may be appropriate. The impact forces from direct collision by ships (as opposed to normal berthing alongside a quay or jetty) are difficult to quantify. However, guidance can be obtained from the IABSE title *On the theory of ship collision against bridge piers* (Saul and Svensson, 1982).

3.9. ENVIRONMENTAL RISKS

It is beyond the scope of this document to examine in detail environmental legislation and its effect on river and estuary engineering works. Instead, this section highlights the principal environmental concerns that now impact or influence river and estuary construction works rather than vice versa. This section does not consider the potential impact of the construction works on the environment. Such an analysis warrants a text in its own right, and for which there are already many published.

The primary mechanism for assessment is to undertake an Environmental (Impact) Assessment. This is an established procedure that has been applied to many river and estuary engineering projects, either formally or informally. When undertaking risk and impact assessments it is important to ensure that the two are consistent (i.e. the environmental specialists are familiar with the construction issues, and the designers with environmental issues). To assist with the identification of possible impacts on the construction works, a list of possible impacts of the works on the environment is given in Appendix 7, along with references for further reading.

Note also that this section has focussed on environmental issues specific to river and estuary engineering only. While issues common to all construction sites, such as noise or traffic, are recognised as common causes for friction within a neighbourhood, they have not been discussed below.

3.9.1. Impact on construction

Table 3.3 and Box 3.26 are typical examples of how recognition of the potential impact of construction works on the environment is likely to modify the design and/or method of construction. Box 3.26 shows an example of 'environmentally sensitive' construction works.

3.9.2. Environmental activists

Other than the possible changes in design and working practice outlined above, an additional risk to the construction process for environmentally 'sensitive'

Table 3.3.   Impact on the environment

Action	Impact on the environment	Measures required in the construction process to minimise adverse impacts on the environment
Design	Channel profile/route — visual intrusion Channel morphology	Construct in 'natural' manner, i.e. irregular, meanders, etc. Design works in harmony with the river characteristics
Changing the river flow regime	Impact on flora, fauna, channel morphology and users such as fisherman, canoeists, etc.	Minimise change or disruption Ensure that adequate warning is given of any changes Make changes progressively rather than abruptly
Excavation and drainage	Release of sediments into river Impact on fisheries Visual impact	Control/limit excavation works in main flow Allow runoff to settle before releasing into river – creation of settlement tanks/lagoons Discharge licence required
	Pollution – use of toxic materials (in water) Site rubbish Spill of pollutant (diesel, etc.)	Restricted choice of materials and application method Control over disposal of rubbish Control over use of potential pollutants Provision of booms/matting for clean up
Earth works	Channel and bank vegetation — damage to or loss of flora	Limited areas and timing of works Modification to original design Construction of soft engineering measures
	Wildlife — loss of habitat, impact on protected species	Restricted working areas/times Provision of alternative habitats/access Alternative design?
	Disturbance of archaeological features	Allow for delay in works programme
Use of river transport	Disturbance, wave action, etc. Disruption to other navigation	Limited access, plant size
Work area in designated site (SSSI, AONB, SAM, etc.)	Various	Tight regulation on practice and procedures

Box 3.26. Environmentally sensitive channel works

(Photograph courtesy of HR Wallingford/Environment Agency)

The photograph shows an excellent example of how works may be designed and constructed to blend with the environment. To improve flood conditions, the discharge capacity of the channel shown was increased by constructing a rectangular concrete channel in place of the natural river channel. The construction methodology and process were greatly influenced by the need to leave as much existing vegetation as possible untouched and for flows to be passed through the site during the works. A year after completion, it is difficult to find any signs of construction, or the permanent works, at the site.

projects is direct action by environmental pressure groups. The aim of such action is ultimately to prevent construction of the works through delay, disruption or sabotage.

While the pressure groups will no doubt have been lobbying against the project at the planning stage, by the time that construction begins, direct action is likely to be the only option remaining for them. Despite having the support of the law, the contractor will need to take preventative measures to avoid delay and disruption. This may entail:

- early/immediate occupation and securing of the construction site
- ensuring tight security around the site with 24-hour surveillance
- ensuring clear access to and from the site for plant and materials
- being aware of, and ready to undertake, legal proceedings for eviction
- preparing contingency plans for removal of protestors
- preparing contingency plans for disruption to any part of the project process.

While some groups will restrict their actions to remain within the law, others will openly flout the law. The level of planning and organisation supporting some groups should not be underestimated. Use of the Internet is becoming common for the distribution of information and planning of protests. The level of information can be extensive, including, for example:

- technical project reports showing the objectives of the project
- anti-project literature
- location maps and plans
- details of protest camps, times and how to join
- names of companies and individuals involved on the project
- suggested actions that could be taken to hinder construction progress.

Health and safety

4

4. Health and safety

4.1. INTRODUCTION

The construction industry's health and safety record is poor when compared to other industries, with 1 in every 100 000 employees involved in a fatal/major injury. There is little statistical information with respect to the performance of the river engineering sector. However, with significant health and safety hazards inherent in river and estuary engineering, the management of many of these hazards is considered more important than for land-based works.

Safety risk is a specialist area of risk management, governed by extensive legislation and regulations, which many consider should be examined quite separately from cost, time, quality and environmental risk. It should be noted that a reduction in health and safety risk usually results in a reduction in the other risks.

This chapter provides a brief overview of relevant issues rather than a detailed explanation of risk and mitigation measures. Appendix 6 contains references on health and safety information, specific to river and estuary engineering.

4.2. RISKS TO HEALTH

Working with water may subject the worker to a variety of health risks, including:

- Sewage — water-borne disease, pollutants and needles
- Weil's disease — serious infection can be fatal, caused by contact with infected rats and by rat or cattle urine
- hypothermia — reduces body temperature, can be life threatening
- fatigue — both mental and physical can reduce performance
- cement dermatitis — skin complaint caused by excessive contact with cement
- musculo-skeletal problems — bad backs, pains, strains, sprains and upper limb disorders
- blue/green algae — origin of naturally occurring toxic substance causing skin rashes, eye irritation, vomiting, diarrhoea, fever and pains in muscles and joints.

Note that cement dermatitis and musculo-skeletal problems are common to many construction projects but working under damp conditions can aggravate these conditions further. For guidance on the ways in which all these health risks may be minimised see Appendix 6.

4.3. RISKS TO SAFETY IN THE RIVER AND ESTUARY ENVIRONMENT

4.3.1. Contributing factors

The nature of work undertaken in river engineering and the working environment itself, combine to create an additional risk to safety, over and above those risks normally present for a land-based project. While the contributing factors may be numerous, the risk to safety may ultimately be reduced to two factors:

- entrapment
- asphyxiation.

Many factors combine to create these risks and some of the most common are listed below. Although some of these risks cannot be removed completely, there are ways of managing and reducing the overall risk.

(a) General work over/in water
Additional risk of:

- fall (with or without injury) and drowning
- accident through use of different and perhaps unfamiliar types of plant
- accident through use of plant in unstable conditions (e.g. bank stability, soil waterlogged)
- accident through interaction with other activities, such as navigation
- plant and workers isolated in water or other liquids (e.g. slurries in lagoons)
- electrocution
- waves or wash from passing boats.

(b) Working within cofferdams
Additional risk of:

- drowning due to failure or overtopping of cofferdam.

(c) Working within a pressurised environment (caissons)
Additional risk of:

- drowning or asphyxiation owing to failure of system
- decompression sickness
- explosion.

(d) Use of different and floating plant
Additional risk of:

- loss of plant and injury owing to misuse
- increased risk of accident owing to plant movement from wave or current action
- increased risk of accident owing to unstable working area (i.e. bank slip, mud — see Box 4.1)

Box 4.1.   Use of plant on unstable ground with insufficient support measures

Working from a stable platform is essential safe practice, particularly for river and estuary engineering where soft banks or ground conditions are commonly encountered.

(Photograph courtesy of HSE)

- instability of barge used as work platform
- injury from passing vessels (unaware of presence).

(*e*) Working with divers
Additional risk of:

- drowning
- injury from other site members (unaware of presence).

(*f*) Use/discovery of explosives
Additional risk of:

- injury through misuse
- injury through discovery of old ordnance (i.e. dredging).

4.3.2. *Mitigation measures*

Various measures may be taken to reduce the risks outlined above. These measures are often basic procedures, rather than high tech or specific solutions, however the HSE find that they are frequently drawing attention to the following actions:

- failure to fence off excavations
- failure to fence off areas, where earth moving vehicles are working

- failure to provide edge protection and lighting, where there is a danger of falling into the water
- dangerous debris being left in areas, open to the public
- failure to wear life jackets, when working over or beside water
- inadequate emergency provisions (e.g. no safety boat, lifebelt or safety lines)
- bad housekeeping (e.g. oil on deck of vessel)
- lack of welfare provisions, resulting in increased health and safety risks
- close proximity of construction/public (e.g. holidaymakers, fishermen) to water.

Boxes 4.2 and 4.3 offer examples of good and bad safety practice.

In some situations, more complex measures will be appropriate to adequately control the risks present. These are likely to comprise automated warning systems and may include:

- measurement of flow velocity
- measurement of water level
- measurement of wave height
- measurement of water temperature
- measurement of water quality
- advance storm warning.

Such systems will be site specific and developed in accordance with the particular risks for the project.

Box 4.2.   Good safety on site, stable working platform

Good safety on site — stable working platform (photographs courtesy of HSE)

Box 4.3. Poor safety on site — weir repairs

Work was undertaken on this weir to prevent further undermining of the structure and erosion of the bank. The channel is constrained with relatively deep water that becomes fast flowing during flood.

(Photographs courtesy of HR Wallingford)

Works were undertaken with little regard to safety or the risk of flood damage. The number of safety regulations broken are too many to list. While the HSE recognises the additional difficulties created by the river or estuary environment this can not be considered as an excuse for poor consideration of basic health and safety issues.

4.3.3. Construction (Design and Management) Regulations 1994

The Construction (Design and Management) Regulations 1994 (CDM) apply to construction projects which employ more than four workers, or last longer than

30 working days or 500 person-days and require that the HSE is notified of all construction projects which are expected to last longer than 30 working days or 500 person-days. This includes any such work carried out in rivers and estuaries from ships or other vessels. The size of most river construction works means that they will be subject to CDM.

The term 'structure' as defined in Regulation 2(1) of CDM is very wide and includes work on any building, steel or concrete structure, dock, harbour, inland navigation, bridge, viaduct, aqueduct, pipe or pipeline, sea-defence works, caisson, earth-retaining structure, and a structure designed to preserve or alter any natural feature.

CDM requires that designs for structures shall avoid foreseeable risks to the health and safety of any person carrying out construction or cleaning work in or on the structure *at any time*, or of any person who may be affected by the work of that person; to combat those risks at source and to give priority to measures which protect all persons at work over those which only protect individuals. CDM therefore applies to the whole life of the structure, including its eventual demolition.

The planning supervisor has to provide the Principal Contractor with a health and safety plan for the construction work, which the latter then develops so that it incorporates:

- the arrangements for managing health and safety during the construction phase (this would include ensuring that subcontractors are fully briefed on the hazards peculiar to the site and its environment)
- assessments prepared by individual contractors, and common arrangements, e.g. emergency procedures and welfare
- arrangements for carrying out his (Principal Contractor) duties
- arrangements for monitoring compliance with health and safety law
- rules for managing health and safety and can be modified as the work progresses according to experience and information received from the contractors.

Note that the information in the paragraphs above present only some aspects of the CDM regulations. These are provided to highlight the important role of CDM regulations but do not set out to be a guide, for which the reader should refer to other publications.

4.3.4. Emergency planning

A fundamental part of safety risk management, is the development and application of emergency plans. Since the two fundamental safety risks in river engineering are entrapment and asphyxiation, both of which are time-dependent, it is essential that emergency measures be undertaken quickly and efficiently.

Many contractors incorporate emergency planning as a routine part of their own health and safety plans, to ensure that in the event of an accident they have at least specified basic procedures to follow. An emergency plan need not be complex, indeed the simpler the plan the more likely it is to be effective. Plans may be as simple as noting down who is responsible for first aid on site to more complex fully-documented procedures for various events, including information such as closest hospitals, access points and methods for contacting emergency services.

For any emergency plan to be effective, the Principal Contractor must not only ensure that the procedures are fully documented, but that all relevant staff are fully briefed and kept up-to-date with any changes or modifications. All project staff should be given a basic briefing so that they know, as a minimum, whom to contact in the event of an accident. There is little merit in having an elaborate emergency plan, if staff are not aware of how to implement it efficiently.

In recognising the importance and need for 'working' emergency plans, the HSE are currently proposing an amendment to the CHSW Regulation 20 (Section 5.4.2). This amendment will require that a written plan, including liaison with emergency services, is required along with the appointment of a person to manage and maintain emergency procedures.

Some of the main issues that should be considered for emergency planning are outlined below.

Emergency services

Construction sites for river and estuary-engineering projects can be remote and unfamiliar to the emergency services. To ensure that the services are able to react quickly to any call and arrive on site within the shortest period of time, it is advisable that briefing meetings are held with the relevant emergency services, in order to plan the most appropriate response to a given situation. Planning may include not only route and method of access, but also the type and magnitude of any emergency response to a call. Such planning can only reduce delays during any event, when time is likely to be critical.

Access

The combination of water, perhaps tidal or in flood, with remote site location can combine to create a serious problem for emergency access (see Box 4.4). Methods and routes of access may change according to flood or tide condition.

These problems may be compounded if the site is spread over a very large area where tidal effects may differ according to location. Since a contractor working in a tidal zone will always plan carefully any construction works around the tides, there is an obligation to consider emergency access at the same time.

Box 4.4. Second Severn Bridge crossing

During construction of the second Severn Bridge crossing, emergency access alternated between vehicle access at low tide and boat access at higher water. At intermediate states where water flooded access routes but currents were high, making boat access difficult and dangerous, the only alternative was to use helicopter access via an appropriately identified platform. This proved vital during an emergency that occurred at just such a tidal state.

Consideration should be given to high-risk activities and the ease with which emergency access may be gained during these events.

Timescale and environment
The state of the tide and weather conditions may dictate what actions should or could be taken. Hence, the appropriate response may depend upon the environmental conditions prevailing at the site, at the time of the event. When dealing with health and safety issues, the time taken to get assistance may make the difference between life and death. Drowning and hypothermia are key hazards in this environment, both of which place a time constraint on the emergency rescue. Rapidly changing tides and currents can pose a significant threat to a trapped worker and the risk of hypothermia should not be underestimated, since the onset and impact can be much quicker in the wet than in a dry environment.

While both of these hazards will never be removed from a river or estuary project, careful planning of construction and emergency operations can reduce the risks. Undertaking the works during the summer season can make a significant difference to the environmental conditions for emergency rescue, as well as the construction programme!

4.4. STATUTORY OBLIGATIONS

This section focuses primarily on health and safety legislation for the UK. However, since the UK is within the EU, it is also subject to the various directives and regulations passed by the EU. Much of the UK legislation has therefore been updated or created in accordance with the appropriate EU Directives, details of which are outlined in Appendix 6. Compliance with UK legislation should therefore ensure compliance for a project within any EU Community. However, the engineer should be aware that local legislation and enforcement bodies applicable for the country where the project is being implemented might modify the terms slightly.

Outside of the EU, health and safety legislation varies from country to country in terms of both coverage and enforcement. The engineer will have to investigate legislation for the individual project and country as appropriate. If in doubt the engineer is well advised to follow best practice as identified within the EU as a starting point for complying with local legislation.

4.4.1. Acts

In general, river and estuary engineering works are subject to the same safety legislation as land-based construction sites. The principal legislation in the UK for this type of work is the Health and Safety at Work Act 1974 (HSWA) the complementary Merchant Shipping Act (MSA) may also apply (see Appendix 6). The MSA will generally apply to river or sea (estuary) going plant, i.e. when they do not form part of the construction site. Once the plant or ship forms part of a construction site (i.e. docked and loading/unloading), then the HSWA will apply (see Box 4.5).

The MSA and associated regulations apply to the master and crew of a UK ship at any time, and generally to other workers on board (unless HSE regulations apply). On non-UK ships, the MSA applies while it is in a UK port. For small vessels (up to 24 m long, carrying no cargo and not more than 12 passengers) there are statutory codes of safety which set minimum standards for construction, machinery, stability, equipment, manning and operation. Many of the vessels covered by these codes also operate on rivers and in estuaries, and

---

Box 4.5. Floating crane assisting in piling work at Thamesport, Hoo, River Medway

(Photograph courtesy of HSE)

The floating crane in the photograph is a German registered ship, working in a UK port — Merchant Shipping Act (and associated regulations) apply to ship, crew and equipment (including the crane). The work activity is piling preparatory to an extension to the jetty — Health and Safety at Work Act (and regulations made under it) apply to the activity and shore-based staff.

HWSA etc. do not normally apply to the ship and equipment *but* the Lifting Operations and Lifting Equipment Regulations 1998 (LOLER) provide that:

- in operations where there is a risk to shore-based workers, a shore employer has to satisfy himself that the MSA requirements in respect of the crane have been complied with
- LOLER Regulation 6 applies to the positioning and installation of the crane
- LOLER Regulation 8 applies to the organisation of the lifting operation.

---

further codes are being developed for inland waterways (instructions for MCA (Maritime and Coastguard Agency) surveyors are already in place).

Under HSWA, the HSE is primarily responsible for enforcing legislation, including CDM, covering the occupational health and safety of shore-based workers engaged in a land-based work activity, and work equipment supplied by the shore as, for example, in the following situations: for workers and equipment employed on construction work on a ship, within UK Territorial Waters; for vessels on rivers or canals whose primary purpose is related to land-based works or undertakings. (Although regulations made under HSWA apply to all workers on non-seagoing ships, in practice, navigation and seaworthiness issues would be enforced by MCA.)

Contravention of health and safety legislation in the river and estuary environment will generally result in prosecution under the HSWA, although prosecution may also refer to the breaching of specific regulations.

4.4.2. Regulations

Health and safety acts are supported by regulations that generally offer more detail than the Act itself. Regulations have the same prosecution power as the Act, hence failure to comply with a regulation, can lead to prosecution under that regulation, rather than the Act. It has been found in practice, that where a regulation has not been complied with, the prosecution will usually refer back to the HSWA, as this is the primary legislation.

Many regulations have been produced in support of the HSWA, in order to update the legislation in line with current practice or EU Directives. There are a few key regulations that are directly applicable to construction risk in river and estuary engineering. These regulations are as follows (a short description of the regulations is given in Appendix 6):

- The Management of Health and Safety at Work Regulations 1992 (MHSW).
- The Construction (Design and Management) Regulations 1994 (CDM).
- The Construction (Health, Safety and Welfare) Regulations 1996 (CHSW).
- Docks Regulations 1988 (DR).
- Dangerous Goods in the Harbour Area Regulations (DGHAR).
- Lifting Operations and Lifting Equipment Regulations (LOLER).
- Provision and Use of Work Equipment Regulations 1998 (PUWER).

4.4.3. Other relevant documentation

The Acts and regulations tend to be concise documents that simply outline the main issues covered by the legislation; there is often little guidance for the practising engineer to ensure compliance with the legislation. The HSE has therefore developed both Approved Code of Practice (ACOP) and guidance documentation to help the engineer understand and apply the legislation.

The ACOP offers methodologies for complying with regulations. Failure to follow the ACOP does not necessarily lead to failure under a regulation but following a code of practice will ensure that regulations are complied with. Although offering additional information in support of codes of practice, neither the ACOP nor the guidance documents have legal standing but would be used to prove that the health and safety legislation had not been followed.

4.4.4. Enforcement

In the UK, the main enforcement body is the HSE who are empowered under the HSWA. The HSE was set up as the operating arm of the Health and Safety Commission (HSC) in 1975. The two bodies report direct to the Secretary of State for the Environment, Transport and the Regions (DETR). Another enforcement body that may become involved in health and safety for a river and estuary engineering project is the MCA. As there is some overlap in legislation at the water margin, HSE, MCA and the Marine Accidents Investigation Branch of the DETR have a Memorandum of Understanding which sets out the respective health and safety enforcement arrangements. This has been recently updated to cover changes which have occurred since it was first agreed, and now includes construction activities.

Enforcement of the legislation is often as important as the legislation itself. In the UK enforcement is via the HSWA through the introduction of regulations under powers within the Act. The UK also has a body of common law and precedents on which courts may draw when deciding cases. This may not be the same in other countries, where they may implement an EU directive in full — 'copy out' — but it does allow the courts to have a greater flexibility in deciding cases.

Outside of the EU, enforcement may again vary significantly and the engineer should seek local advice to ensure that their safety policies or standards are appropriate and acceptable in the host country. As a starting point, the engineer should expect a similar level of enforcement to that practised in the UK.

—

Insurance

5. Insurance

5.1. INTRODUCTION

Insurance is a method of risk transfer and a mechanism for smoothing out costs of losses, and should follow the risk management process of risk identification, control and retention. It is used to guarantee, at a regular annual cost, or at a fixed rate for a specific one-off project, the future financial stability against the consequences of irregular non-speculative business risk. It is important in river and estuary engineering, as these irregular non-speculative risks can be very significant.

There will be numerous companies with an interest in the risks associated with a construction project. These will include the employer (client), contractor, subcontractors, consulting engineer, designer, manufacturers, suppliers, hauliers and shippers. Each company will need to undertake a risk management exercise to identify, control and consider retention and/or insurance of his risks. Some risks will require compulsory insurance by law (e.g. Employers Liability and Road Traffic Act cover) or by contract (e.g. Contract Works and Public Liability cover). The final decision on whether to insure other risks will be affected by:

- the company's size and risk transfer philosophy
- the probability of the risk occurring and its financial effect
- the availability and cost of insurance.

Some companies may elect to carry a high level of monetary self-insurance (where not otherwise restricted by law or contract) to reduce insurance premium costs.

The insurance market is cyclical with premiums increasing and some insurers withdrawing from certain risks following poor results and then premiums reducing and insurers entering or re-entering the market when results improve. The volatility of results in the construction market has seen a number of insurers (including some major companies) withdrawing from UK single project and overseas construction risks.

Generally, the benefit of good risk management in the construction industry will reduce the uncertainties faced by insurers and improve insurer confidence thus making for a more stable market. Improved and more consistent results will inevitably lead to premium benefits for those buying insurance.

5.2. TYPES OF INSURANCE

Table 5.1 summarises most of the risks arising in connection with a construction project, the companies who are likely to be responsible, and the types and availability of insurance.

5.2.1. Contractors' All Risks Insurance

Defects
The terms of contract will usually make the contractor responsible for correcting defects in the works at his own cost. Depending on the scope of the contract, these defects may be due to faulty design, workmanship, materials, plan or specification. The Contractors' All Risks Insurance policy which usually provides cover up to the end of the defects liability or maintenance period (not exceeding 24 months) will have a defects exclusion wording which will vary from a total exclusion of all damage due to defects to a less restrictive exclusion of the costs of improvements following damage due to defects. The most commonly found wording excludes damage to defective portions of the works (including all associated repair works) but not damage to other parts of the works arising from such defects.

The following are some *special exclusions and warranties* which may be applied to Contractors' All Risks Insurance for river and estuary projects. It should be noted that these will usually be the subject of negotiation with the outcome dependent upon each risk and the risk management and design criteria. Insurers will seek to exclude inevitable risks and this is the main purpose of these exclusions and warranties.

Misaligned piles
Cost of rectifying, removing, repairing or replacing:

- misaligned foundation piles and/or sheet pile constructions
- lock disconnected or distortion of sheet piles during placing
- leakage of seams, penetrations of joints and connections of sheet piles.

Dewatering
Costs and expenses incurred in dewatering, even if the quantities of water originally expected are exceeded, or expenses for additional protections and facilities for the discharge or run-off of underground water.

Normal action of the sea/normal tidal action
Loss of, or damage to, the insured property caused by normal action of the sea or tides. A definition of 'normal action of the sea' or 'tides' worthy of consideration for insurance purposes is 'that behaviour of the tide current and wave action suggested by available marine and meteorological data for the month and location for an agreed return period' (typically between 1 in 1 years and 1 in 10 years, depending upon the risk and design criteria).

Table 5.1. Construction risks, responsibility and insurance type

Risks	Companies with potential responsibility	Insurance
Physical loss of, or damage to, contract materials and components during: (a) manufacture (b) works testing	Manufacturer Manufacturer	Property — readily available Works testing breakdown insurance — very limited availability
Physical loss of, or damage to, permanent and temporary works during transportation and temporary storage offsite	Manufacturer/Supplier Contractor Subcontractor Employer (Client)	Goods-in-transit, Marine Cargo, Contractors' All Risks — readily available
Physical loss of, or damage to, permanent and temporary works during construction, testing/ commissioning, and defects liability or maintenance period	Contractor Subcontractor Employer (Client)	Contractors' All Risks — readily available
	With possible rights of recourse against	Products Guarantee — very limited availability
	Manufacturer/Supplier Designer/Consulting Engineer	Professional Indemnity — available
Physical loss of, or damage to, owned construction plant, temporary buildings and employers effects and Legal Liability for physical loss of, or damage to, hired-in plant and temporary buildings and for continued hiring charges during storage, transport and on-site working	Contractor Subcontractor Employer (Client) Haulier Shipping Company	Contractors' All Risks Contractors Plant Hand-Plant Employers' Effects Marine Cargo — readily available
Physical loss of, or damage to, ships, vessels, barges, etc., involved in transportation or site construction activities	Shipping companies	Marine Hull Insurance — readily available
Physical loss of, or damage to, vehicles registered for use on public roads	All companies	Motor (comprehensive insurance) — readily available
Liability for payment of liquidated damages to the Employer (Client) as a result of delays	Contractor/subcontractor	Liquidated damage insurance only for delays due to physical loss of, or damage to, the works — very limited availability. Penalties and fines always excluded

Table 5.1.   continued

Risks	Companies with potential responsibility	Insurance
Loss of profit or revenue arising from delays in the project	Employer (Client)	Advanced Business Interruption Insurance following physical loss of, or damage to, the works — limited availability for this type of project
Physical loss of, or damage to, property, works and plant due to terrorist acts:		
(*a*) in Great Britain	Contractor Subcontractor Employer (Client)	Property, Constructors' All Risks up to £100 000 with buy-backs over £100 000
(*b*) in Northern Ireland	Contractor Subcontractor Employer (Client)	Government fund
War risks	All companies	Only available under Marine Insurances
Death of, or injury to, directors, managers and employees	All companies	Personal accident — readily available but limited availability for site workers

Return flood period

Loss of, or damage to, the insured property caused by flooding having an agreed return period (typically between 1 in 1 years and 1 in 10 years, depending upon the risk and design criteria).

Over-topping of cofferdams

Loss or damage caused by overtopping of cofferdams.

Re-dredging

Costs and expenses in re-dredging or reprofiling of any dredged trench or area unless necessitated by indemnifiable damage to other portions of the contract works.

Impact by shipping

Loss or damage caused by impact of shipping. Vessels carry a limited liability by law and construction insurers will consider this risk on receipt of relevant information on shipping movements and risk control measures. Insurers will normally require the insured to retain a significant level of monetary self-insurance for this risk. The two laws that cover this particular aspect are the Merchant Shipping Act 1995 and the Convention on Limitation of Liability for Maritime Claims 1976. The losses are calculated on a complex formula based on the tonnage of the vessel and the number of transits of the affected waters.

Loss of fill
Loss of fill unless accompanied by other indemnifiable damage.

Pipe pulling
Warranted that during pipe pulling or towing operations the maximum yield stress exerted on the pipe or pulling wires shall not exceed 85% of the specified minimum yield of the pipe material.

Radiography of welds
Warranted that all welds on steel pipelines will be subjected to radiography.

Yield testing (steel pipelines)
It is understood and agreed that damage occurring during high-level hydrostatic testing is not insured unless it is demonstrated by the insured, beyond reasonable doubt, that the yield pressure at no time exceeded 90% of the specified minimum yield or that it exceeded this percentage solely due to failure of the equipment employed for control and instrumentation during the test.

5.3. CURRENT PRACTICE IN THE EVALUATION OF RISKS BY THE INSURANCE MARKET

5.3.1. Evaluation of the hazards

In the UK, brokers who obtain from insurers insurance on the best possible terms (including cover, premium, service) mainly supply the construction insurance market. In the case of project insurance, this is usually undertaken at tender stage and finalised at the time of winning the contract, with the technical information relevant to the river and estuary construction project being provided by the construction company. The insurer has to assess this information to ascertain the actual risks involved, in order to propose terms to the construction firm. These terms will depend on:

- the underwriter's skills in evaluating the hazards in the construction industry
- the underwriter's experience of river and estuary construction risks, including:
  - knowledge of the hazards related to the structure type
  - knowledge of the hazards related to different phases of the project
  - knowledge of influence of physical conditions (e.g. currents, tidal surge, waves, etc.)
  - knowledge of probability of occurrence of these hazards during the total construction period
- data records available (e.g. flow, levels, etc., records at the site)
- time available for the evaluation

○ funds available for the evaluation
● market forces present at the time.

The underwriter is rarely a technical expert, although most major insurance companies employ at least one civil engineer on which they can call for guidance. They will rely on the adequacy of the information supplied by the insured and on their own experience in assessing the level of risk and the insurance terms and conditions commensurate with the risk. It is important that he has confidence in the ability and experience of the contractor and past loss history is an important factor. River and estuary works create higher than normal risk levels and premiums, with self-insurance sums reflecting this fact, especially with regard to major risks including water, storm, tempest, flood, landslip, subsidence, collapse and, in some overseas countries, earthquake.

There is some information available to help the underwriters evaluate these hazards. (Indeed it is hoped that this guide will go a long way towards this goal.) At present, insurers will mainly use:

● information supplied by broker
● insurer's own surveyors
● historical records of similar projects
● reference books
● subjective assessments
● the previous claims records of the contractor
● in-house engineers.

The Insurance Institute of London publishes a guide entitled *Construction and erection insurance report* (Insurance Institute of London, 1985) which includes some information on risks related to river and estuary engineering.

5.3.2. Evaluation of the risk-exposure level

There has been little published guidance to date for the insurance industry or others involved in construction as to what weather conditions the contractor should take account of when designing their temporary works, e.g. flood levels, maximum tidal surge level. However, clients will often stipulate design criteria and may require contractors to design temporary works to higher standards than would be strictly necessary for the project. Insurers have to determine whether the relative level of risk exposure is normal or otherwise. A commonly used figure is the 1 in 10-year event, but this is arbitrary. Note also that the 1 in 10-year event may comprise not only extreme flood events but also a combination of different types of extreme events, e.g. a prolonged period of very low flow. The risk exposure will depend directly upon the length of construction period. Given reliable data an estimation of risk exposure may be calculated (see Section 2.7).

Where records are available it is important to use as long a period as possible to ensure that the selected design event accurately represents the real situation. Insurers should check that contractors are utilising the most up-to-date records.

In the absence of any records, use of predictive models are likely to provide the best alternative.

Insurers should also be aware of the programming approach that the contractor is taking to the works. An experienced contractor will be optimising the available weather windows, to ensure that critical and vulnerable works are carried out during periods of statistically-likely good weather.

5.4. AIDE MEMOIRE FOR INSURANCE ISSUES

The following are key issues when considering construction insurance:

- Insurance is a risk transfer mechanism which should only follow good risk management practice.
- When seeking insurance for a project, the provision of all relevant underwriting information, which will include risk reducing factors, will achieve the best premium levels for the proposed project.
- Levels/types of cover and amounts of self-insurance should be decided in accordance with the needs of each individual company.
- All parties should be aware of their, and others, legal and contractual responsibilities for loss or damage, defects, liabilities and insurance. Careful attention should be given to non-standard contracts and amendments to standard forms.
- If another party is responsible for arranging 'joint names' insurance, ensure that the level of cover and self-insured amount (excess) suits your own company's insurance philosophy.
- Each party should be aware of the terms of any insurance cover (including limits, exclusions, warranties and self-insured amounts).
- Joint Venture, Private Finance Initiative (PFI) (now Private Public Partnership) and Design Build Finance Operate (DBFO) projects will require special insurance arrangements and should be referred to your normal insurance advisor.
- Notify claims promptly to insurers with all relevant information to facilitate speedy settlement.
- Better risk-management practices by the construction industry will lead to improved insurance results and a lowering of market premiums.
- Better risk management by the individual contractor will lead to less incidents, a reduction in cost escalations and will reduce the potential for penalties for delay. It will create insurer confidence in the contractor's professionalism with the benefit of lower premiums. This will lead to enhanced opportunities for pre-qualification for tenders, more competitive tendering and improved profits.

Procurement

6

6. Procurement

6.1. CONTEXT

6.1.1. Significance of procurement

This chapter discusses risk issues in relation to current procurement methods and contractual arrangements. The guidance given concentrates on current practices within England and Wales, although the principles are applicable within the UK and on international projects. The chapter should not be used as a main source of information when considering procurement methods, as other publications, particularly in relation to publicly-funded projects, cover procurement in more detail.

Other sections of this manual have shown that river and estuary projects have different and relatively high levels of risk compared with the majority of land-based projects. Particular problems that generate substantial construction risk are:

- high river flows
- wind, waves and water levels
- ground conditions.

Procurement and contract strategies which do not allow for quantifying, minimising and properly allocating these specific risks can therefore result in increased construction risk to the project, with associated additional costs and poor achievement of project objectives.

It is therefore essential that the procurement process results in:

- The selection and appointment of consultants and contractors with appropriate experience to foresee, minimise and manage risks associated with the project (including foreseeable project variations or alternatives).
- Contractual arrangements that properly allocate risks to those best able to manage them.
- Financial returns on work which allow time for proper risk management.
- Robust methods of working which minimise risk, and reward for the acceptance of risk.

The adoption of a competitive tendering process, with automatic selection of the lowest tender, has not always achieved these objectives in the past.

6.1.2. The project team

Much has been written in recent years on innovative procurement strategies, particularly since publication of the Latham Review, *Constructing the team*, in 1994 which included the stated objective of achieving a reduction in the level of construction costs of 30%. To achieve such savings, Latham proposed a complete rethink of the relationship between the various parties to the construction process. The traditional procurement strategies and contractual arrangements had been largely adversarial and had not always provided a good basis for the contracting parties to gain good value from the work involved.

The late 1990s have seen both the public and private sector investigate the potential construction cost savings suggested by Latham, and to adopt the vision of best practice procurement, with the aim of obtaining improved value for money and improved management of risk. Organisations like the Environment Agency have now moved towards framework agreements and partnering, with the aim of forging a closer relationship with contractors, subcontractors and suppliers with the skills, experience and attitude to ensure the delivery of projects of high quality, to time and to budget.

The previous chapters have shown that the management of risk is improved by systematic analysis of risk, followed by mitigation, allocation and control of the residual risks. Ideally all members of the project team should contribute to this process, including the client, designer, contractor and end-user. Early involvement of the contractor has frequently been difficult to achieve in the traditional procurement route, but some clients are now commissioning advice from contractor organisations, even though they may not eventually be the chosen contractor. This has advantages for the value-engineering and risk-management processes, using workshops to draw on the available expertise.

6.1.3. The role and aims of the client in the procurement process

The client, and particularly the extent to which their procurement procedures may be prescribed and the level of expertise available in the organisation, will influence the approach to risk in the procurement process. Clients can be either from the public or private sectors.

Although the larger clients, particularly those such as the Environment Agency, who deal with large numbers of river and estuary projects, employ staff with a good range of experience of this type of work, the majority of the detailed work is carried out by consultants and some contractors. Much of the responsibility for the control and management of risk therefore lies with private sector consultants and contractors. However, this responsibility may be modified by the terms of the appointment. In some cases clients in both the private and public sectors may wish to see cost certainty and the transfer to others of the majority of the risks, whereas other arrangements can see agreement on the sharing of residual risks.

The largest funder of river and estuary projects is the public sector, and the December 1997 publication from HM Treasury *Procurement guidance* (the first

---

> **Box 6.1. Public policy commitment, extract from *Procurement guidance* (HM Treasury, 1997)**
>
> Departments should make a public policy commitment to give a client lead to the industry by:
>
> - openly finding out which designers, constructors or specialist suppliers are the best;
> - tendering with the aim of getting those who offer the best service;
> - working with their people as a team not opponents, and
> - making no compromises with people or suppliers who are unco-operative or adversarial.
>
> *Key points for senior management*
> UK government policy is that all procurement should be on the basis of value for money (VFM) and not lowest price alone. Consultants and contractors therefore should be appointed on this basis.
>
> Robust mechanisms specific to each project should be developed to evaluate the quality and price (whole-life cost) components of each bid in a fair, transparent and accountable manner.
>
> The selection and award processes are separate and distinct.
>
> Key criteria for both processes should include:
>
> - partnering and team working, and
> - evidence of skills ability (for contractors).
>
> The client department must lead the project at all times, even after the appointment of a client adviser, project manager or other consultant.
>
> A VFM framework should be established for each project which ensures a structured approach to planning and managing a project from inception to completion.

in a series of publications) gives clear advice to government departments. They hope this will also give a clear lead to the whole industry to adopt efficient procurement procedures. The summary statements for this document are at the heart of the current policy and Box 6.1 reproduces this useful guidance in full.

6.1.4. Project funding

Project funding will influence the management of risk, particularly under the following circumstances:

- Projects where budgets are limited in the early stages of a scheme may restrict the investigations necessary to identify, minimise and manage risk.
- The need for cost certainty may mean that some residual risk, which would normally be deemed acceptable, must be designed out, even if this results in an increased project cost.
- The need to establish and expand an annual budget in the public sector has sometimes resulted in an inappropriate early start date to maximise expenditure in a financial year. This often has consequences in respect of weather conditions or incomplete investigations. Similarly, over-expenditure on a project has resulted in work suspension, to avoid exceeding annual

budgets. These pressures may adversely affect the management of construction risk in some projects and should be taken into account in deciding the procurement strategy and, in some cases, the detailed design of the permanent works.

6.2. PROCUREMENT FRAMEWORK

A number of procurement strategies are available to a client with river or estuary engineering projects. These strategies in turn affect the timing of the selection of the eventual contractor either early or late in the project.

Five principal strategies can be identified, although each may have a number of variants and may employ a range of forms of contract.

- *Designer led*. Separate appointment, either based on experience or more usually through a tendering process to appoint a consultant and a contractor, the contractor being appointed late in the process.
- *Design and Build*. Such procurement strategies have been popular within the construction industry but have not yet been extensively used within the river and estuary engineering sector. With this procurement strategy, it is essential that the client's objectives can be clearly defined. This is not always easy in river and estuary engineering projects where environmental or landowner interests or economic justification issues can significantly amend the initial proposals.
- *Prime contracting* is a new development of design and build put forward by HM Treasury Procurement Guide No. 5 (HM Treasury, 1999b) as a preferred approach to procurement in the public sector. Its relevance and application in river and estuary engineering has yet to be resolved but it may be of interest to note that it has the following key features:

  o a single point of responsibility (the 'Prime Contractor') coming between the client and the supply chain
  o the Prime Contractor having the demonstrable ability to bring together and manage all key members of the supply chain to meet the client's requirements (this might be met, for example, by the Prime Contractor having in place strategic partnering arrangements with the first tier suppliers, including design consultants)
  o the Prime Contractor developing a whole life cost model before construction begins.

- *Management fee*. Under this approach, the lead contractor manages the construction process for a fee, with the actual work undertaken by other contractors. Designers and other consultants are appointed separately. The approach has been used primarily on large commercial building work, and has not had significant use in the UK on coastal or river engineering projects. There are two principal variants:

- ○ in *construction management* construction work is undertaken by 'trade contractors' employed directly by the client and the Construction Manager often also manages the design process
- ○ in *management contracting* construction is undertaken by 'works contractors' subcontracted to the 'Management Contractor'.

- *Design Build Finance and Operate (DBFO)*. This approach has a number of alternative names and guises, including BOOT (Build Own Operate Transfer) and, in the public sector, PFI (Public Finance Initiative) or PPPP (Public-Private Partnering Programme). In this approach the funds for the capital cost of the project are raised by the private sector and the private sector contractor remains responsible for the management of the asset. The approach encourages the consideration of whole-life cost and of construction and future risks to the structure. The process is generally only applicable to multi-million pound schemes, again where objectives are clear and to date has only been adopted by the Environment Agency on one river engineering project (Broadlands).

A comparison of the advantages and disadvantages of these different forms of procurement (excluding the new development of prime contracting) is given in Table 6.1. All parties should be clear regarding the *potential* risks to which they are exposed under the selected strategy and what risks it may be appropriate to transfer or share.

It is particularly important that the commonly occurring risks associated with river and estuary engineering projects are clearly allocated.

- *High river flow* risks should be clearly defined, probably in terms of a specified maximum event (e.g. 10-year return period event) over a specified period (e.g. a particular month of the year), and the contractor can then clearly price the project on the basis of catering for all flows up to the particular monthly (or other period) values. Vague definitions such as 'normal' river flows should be avoided and precise formulations included such as that adopted in the *Engineering and construction contract* (ICE, 1995) compensation events.
- *Wind, wave and water levels* should be treated in a similar way to high river flows.
- *Ground condition* risks can be transferred completely to the contractor, for example, by omitting standard unforeseen ground condition clauses from standard forms of contract. However, it is generally better to reduce the risk to a manageable level by carrying out sufficient site investigation at an early stage in the project. At this point it is generally easier to carry out this investigation in a cost effective and timely manner and, where several projects are involved, economies of scale can be achieved.

In making decisions about passing any of these risks on to contractors or others, clients should be aware of the following, generally applicable, principles:

Table 6.1. Comparison of procurement strategies

Procurement strategy	Advantages	Disadvantages	Other implications
Designer led	• Extensive usage within industry • Suitable for single and/or smaller projects • Ongoing development of project concept possible	• Buildability often not well-considered • Can lead to confrontational relationships • Risk allocation is often pre-defined by standard form of contract adopted (e.g. *ICE 6th Edition*) and these forms may not suit the specific problems of flow and ground conditions prevalent in river engineering • Price uncertainty	• Need to commission advice on buildability from contractor organisations • Need for teamwork and partnering to overcome potential for confrontation
Design and Build	• Increased price certainty • Project buildability generally well considered; hence risk to project programme reduces • All construction risk can be unambiguously transferred to contractor	• Limited experience in use of method in river engineering • Project must be well defined before contract commences, including relationship to broader river or estuary management issues • Price certainty/control on capital cost may be at the expense of operating/maintenance costs, leading to increased whole-life costs	• Need to incorporate *all* client requirements in project brief

Procurement method	Advantages	Disadvantages	Notes
Management fee (e.g. construction management; management contracting)	• More flexibility for client in project design-process than in design and build • More control over project team (in construction management) • Efficient allocation of construction risk • Contractor and client have similar objectives • Works well for large or long time-scale projects	• Lack of early price certainty • Multiple parties make teamwork more complex • Rarely used in river and estuary engineering	• Management fee contracting does not obviously suit river and estuary engineering with the limited number of disciplines involved. It more obviously suits projects where many disciplines and/or trades are involved and where completion on time is more important than price certainty
Design Build Finance and Operate (DBFO). Examples include BOOT (Build Own Operate Transfer) PFI (Private Finance Initiative), now Public/Private Partnering Programme (PPPP)	• Suitable for larger contracts or groups of contracts (such as the Broadlands scheme) • Low initial client-cost. Capital expenditure is effectively spread over a number of years to suit private client cash-flow or public-sector funding arrangements • Should ensure minimum whole-life cost over period of contractor responsibility for asset	• Extensive and costly tendering procedures and contract negotiations required, including significant legal costs • Limited number of suitable river and estuary engineering schemes available	• May require groups of schemes to be packaged together to be cost-effective

- The more the client passes risk on to others, the less control he has over its management.
- All those required to accept risk must be paid for doing so, and thus have the opportunity to price for it.

6.3. SELECTION OF PROJECT PARTICIPANTS

As explained in Section 6.1.3 above, it is now UK government policy that project participants should be selected with reference to quality/ability as well as to price, i.e. on the basis of best value. This applies to contractors as well as consultants. Public-sector clients must now seek 'best value', and obtaining the lowest price is no longer recognised as automatically providing that value. It may be that for a small well-defined project the process of pre-qualification of contractors on the basis of quality/ability might be as good a way as any of achieving value, but this should never be an automatic assumption.

There are a number of very useful guides that have been published recently which summarise best practice in this area.

- *Value by competition — a guide to the competitive procurement of consultancy services for construction*, CIRIA SP117
- *Selecting contractors by value*, CIRIA SP150
- HM Treasury Procurement Practice and Development (PPD) Guidances

  - No. 1 *Essential requirements for construction procurement* (1997)
  - No. 2 *Value for money in construction procurement* (1997)
  - No. 3 *Appointment of consultants and contractors* (1997)
  - No. 4 *Teamworking, partnering and incentives* (1999)
  - No. 5 *Procurement strategies* (1999)
  - No. 6 *Financial aspects of projects* (1999)

- Construction Industry Board (CIB) reports of working groups WG1 to WG12, published by Thomas Telford (1997).

The user of this manual should make reference to these both for clearer guidance and also, in the case of the CIRIA documents, for the excellent toolkits which they offer to assist in the valuation of quality in relation to price.

6.3.1. Pre-qualification

Quality-related pre-qualification or quantity evaluation in a quality-price assessment of tenders at the selection stage should include consideration in a balanced and auditable way of the competence, resources and experience of the consultant or contractor (as appropriate). CIRIA SP150 (CIRIA, 1998) identifies appropriate ways of assessing these under the following headings.

- Technical knowledge and skill

- Skill and commitment in managing

  - time
  - cost
  - value
  - quality
  - risk
  - health and safety
  - environmental issues

- Effectiveness of internal organisation
- Attitude and culture
- Quality of proposed human resources
- Quality of supply chain management.

Pre-qualification can lead to consultants or contractors being placed on 'approved lists', which can be administered through specific organisations like Construction Line. However, the danger with approved lists is that there will be insufficient discrimination between contractors when it comes to project-specific quality, particularly bearing in-mind that river and estuary engineering projects may only occasionally arise with some clients. Thus there is a need to reconsider these criteria in relation to subsequent project-specific prequalifications.

6.3.2. Selection

The VFM principles set out in Section 6.1.3 are now considered best practice. These practices are now enshrined within government policy and are entirely consistent with EU directives. However, it is important to appreciate that this has not always been the case. Indeed, a conscious effort is still required in many cases by clients to ensure that such principles are followed. This section explores how these ideas affect the selection of both consultants and contractors.

Before the 1980s consultants within the UK were normally selected for the feasibility, design and supervision stages of a project by public authorities and private industry on recommendation from previous work for the client or similar clients. This tended to encourage the use of consultants who had a good grasp of local conditions and the type of work involved in the project, without necessarily improving the management of the local and project risks involved.

Competitive tendering for professional services was introduced, particularly from the late 1980s onwards, to demonstrate that these services were obtained at lowest costs, often to meet national and European directives. Consultants were often asked to assume responsibility for some of the client's risk, but the risk was often poorly defined and the consultant was not always given the authority to manage it.

Experience of this kind of competitive tendering has now shown that the emphasis on lowest price in the selection of consultants has often not given best value to clients, particularly in respect of whole-life project costs. In some cases, consultants would adopt expensive over-conservative capital works designs to reduce risk of design failure and to reduce design times to match their fees. In the worst cases, low fees led to designs of inferior quality which then exposed the client to subsequent unexpected high maintenance or repair costs.

The second half of the 1990s has seen moves to consider technical competency, experience and quality as important selection criteria as well as the tendered consultancy fees. More innovative methods of operating have been introduced, including term consultancies, framework agreements (see Section 6.3.3) and partnering (see Section 6.4). This is now developing into arrangements that ensure that project staff are both:

- as able to identify risks in river and estuary projects as consultants were before the 1980s, but also are
- experienced enough to minimise, allocate and manage those risks.

This is often achieved by consultants becoming part of an integrated project team including the client and other professionals. In particular, contractors may be appointed to such teams to advise on buildability. The *Professional services contract* (ICE, 1998) which emphasises such team working and co-operation is now frequently being used to support such an approach.

The selection of contractors for construction works has seen major changes over the past few years. In the past, contractors submitted their tenders based on client- or consultant-prepared Bills of Quantities, Specifications and Drawings. Almost without exception in the public sector, the lowest bid was then accepted — generally as it was the easiest means of achieving apparent accountability — and this led to such an approach being enshrined in standing orders or similar official guidance. Such choices were sometimes to the detriment of the resulting quality of the works and the time taken to achieve completion. Final account cost over-runs on the originally tendered price were thus common (although many over-runs were also affected by lack of, or poor, site and design information resulting in additional work and extension of time).

Nowadays, the approach recommended by CIRIA SP150 is to select contractors by value. This involves selecting the contractor

'who offers the best value to a project measured more than simply the lowest price'. Principally, it involves:

- identifying what represents 'value' to the particular client in a particular project
- defining what contractors must offer if they are to add to that value
- making the contractor's potential to add value (which will be some combination of the factors set out in Section 6.3.1 above) to the main selection criterion.

Contractors' prices for their services will inevitably remain a consideration but not necessarily the most significant, and never the only one.

In addition to detailed guidance on selection criteria and scoring systems for selection, CIRIA SP150 also identifies and describes in detail two principal models for the timing of the contractor's selection.

(*a*) A single preferred contractor is selected at an early stage of the project to contribute to its development.

(*b*) Competition is maintained between contractors until a late stage with a specific contractor selected only in the step prior to construction.

Although there is pressure in the public sector to adopt the second model to demonstrate competition on price, this is not always the case, especially if the parties to the project are able and willing to approach it in an open and collaborative manner. While contractors can and should be involved in the second model (either via presenting alternative tenders or by an ongoing dialogue during tender document preparation), the first model probably offers the greatest potential for a contractor to add value.

It should be noted that even though the selection criteria identified in Section 6.3.1 may have been used in a pre-qualification process, they should again be considered at final selection stage. In all cases, clients should be aware of their responsibilities under the CDM regulations, when appointing a Principal Contractor, to ensure he is competent and has sufficient resources, including time, to perform his health and safety duties.

6.3.3. Framework agreements

Framework agreements have been used in the public sector where the public bodies want particular services. The agreements may be competitively tendered (the public sector requirement) or negotiated between a select list of tenderers. The main advantage such agreements offer is that, once they have been set up, further extensive pre-qualification and tendering procedures are eliminated for the remainder of the framework agreement contract period. Project-related construction risk does not necessarily have to be specifically considered at the time of setting up of the agreements. However, if the agreement is directly related to a particular project (or group of projects of similar type), the risk issues, the apportionment between the parties and their subsequent management may be incorporated in some way into the agreement.

6.4. PARTNERING

There are a number of very useful guides that have recently been published which summarise best practice in this area. The user of this manual should make reference to these for clearer guidance:

- *Partnering in the public sector — a toolkit for the implementation of post award, project specific partnering on construction projects* (ECI, 1997)
- *Construction procurement by Government. An Efficiency Unit Scrutiny* (Efficiency Unit, Cabinet Officer, 1995)
- *Trusting the team: the best practice guide to partnering in construction* (Bennett and Jayes, 1995)
- *Partnering in the Team* (CIB, 1997i)

The European Construction Institute (ECI) in their invaluable document *Partnering in the public sector* (ECI, 1997) define partnering as follows:

> Partnering is both an attitude of mind and a series of procedures which commit the parties involved in a construction project to focus on creative co-operation and to work to avoid confrontation. Its essential component is trust. The Reading Construction Forum have defined it as follows: 'Partnering is a managerial approach used by two or more organisations to achieve specific business objectives by maximising the effectiveness of each participant's resources. The approach is based on mutual objectives, an agreed method of problem resolution and an active search for continuous measurable improvements.'
>
> Essentially . . . partnering is a generic term. It embraces a range of practices of varying formality, designed to promote more co-operative working between contracting parties.

The ECI go on to identify two main forms of partnering:

- strategic alliances or term partnering
- project alliances or project-specific partnering.

The variation of the latter which ECI view as being more suited to the public sector is

- post-award project-specific partnering.

It is a common misconception that the requirements of EU procurement directives, which provide for open and fair competition, preclude partnering arrangements as being incompatible with open competition. One official comment will suffice:

> 'Partnering is acceptable under EU rules if
>
> - it is competitively arranged
> - the client's needs and objectives are clearly stated
> - the contract is for a specified period, and
> - safeguards for future competition are incorporated.'
>
> (*Construction procurement by Government. An Efficiency Unit Scrutiny* (HMSO, 1995) – 'The Levene Report')

As well as attitudes of commitment, fairness and trust from all those involved, partnering typically involves the following:

- *selection procedures* to ensure parties are compatible and committed
- *a partnering workshop* to align objectives and set ground rules
- a non-contractual *partnering charter* describing how the parties intend to conduct themselves
- *open and full communications* between the parties to an agreed structure
- continuous monitoring by an agreed *evaluation procedure*
- an agreed *dispute avoidance/resolution procedure* designed to resolve issues at the earliest possible opportunity at the lowest possible level of authority
- *a continuous improvement procedure.*

It should be noted that outside the public sector, partnering or alliancing is often associated with target-cost contracts. These involve establishing a target-cost during post-tender negotiations (based on tendered rates). If the project is subsequently delivered for less than the target cost then the partnering or alliancing partners receive a pre-agreed percentage of the savings — the 'gain-share'. Conversely, where the target cost is exceeded, then each partner will suffer his share of the additional costs (or losses) in the 'pain-share'. This financial incentive process helps to gain additional commitment to the partnering process.

References

7

7. References

Association of Project Managers (APM). Simon, Hillson and Newland, eds (1997). *Project risk, analysis and management (PRAM) guide*. APM Group Ltd.

Bennett, J. and Jayes, S. (1995). *Trusting the team: the best practice guide to partnering in construction*. Reading Centre for Strategic Studies in Construction.

Breusers, H. N. C. and Raudkivi, A. J. (1991). *Scouring, hydraulic structures design manual*. IAHR, Balkema, Rotterdam.

British Standards Institution. (1984). *Code of practice for maritime structures*. BS 6349: Part 1: 1984.

Carter. B., *et al*. (1995). *RISKMAN — The European project risk management methodology*. Blackwell, Cambridge.

Carter, B., Hancock, T., Morin, J.-M. and Robins, N. (1995). *Introducing RISKMAN methodology, the European project risk management method*. Blackwell, Cambridge.

Chadwick, A. and Morfett, J. (1995). *Hydraulics in civil and environmental engineering*. E. & F. N. Spon, London.

Chow, V. T. (1973). *Open channel hydraulics*. McGraw Hill.

Construction (Design and Management) Regulations 1994 (CDM Regulations). (SI 1989: 1903). HMSO, London.

Construction Industry Board. (1997a). *Briefing the Team: a guide to a better briefing for clients*. Report of Working Group 1. Thomas Telford, London.

Construction Industry Board. (1997b). *Constructing Success: code of practice for clients of the construction industry*. Report of Working Group 2. Thomas Telford, London.

Construction Industry Board. (1997c). *Code of practice for the selection of main contractors*. Report of Working Group 3. Thomas Telford, London.

Construction Industry Board. (1997d). *Code of practice for the selection of subcontractors*. Report of Working Group 3. Thomas Telford, London.

Construction Industry Board. (1997e) *Selecting consultants for the team: balancing quality and price*. Report of Working Group 4. Thomas Telford, London.

Construction Industry Board. (1997f). *Framework for a national register for consultants*. Report of Working Group 4. Thomas Telford, London.

Construction Industry Board (1997g). *Framework for a national register for contractors*. Report of Working Group 5. Thomas Telford, London.

Construction Industry Board. (1996a). *Training the team*. Report of Working Group 6. Thomas Telford, London.

Construction Industry Board. (1996b). *Constructing a better image*. Report of Working Group 7. Thomas Telford, London.

Construction Industry Board (1996c). *Tomorrow's team: women and men in construction*. Report of Working Group 8. Thomas Telford, London.

Construction Industry Board. (1996d). *Educating the professional team*. Report of Working Group 9. Thomas Telford, London.

Construction Industry Board. (1997h) *Liability law and latent defects insurance*. Report of Working Group 10. Thomas Telford, London.

Construction Industry Board. (1996e). *Towards a 30% productivity improvement in construction*. Report of Working Group 11. Thomas Telford, London.

Construction Industry Board. (1997i). *Partnering in the team*. Report of Working Group 12. Thomas Telford, London.

Construction Industry Research and Information Association (CIRIA). Simm, J. D., ed. (1991). *Manual on the use of rock in coastal and shoreline engineering*. CIRIA Special Publication 83/CUR Report No 154.

Construction Industry Research and Information Association (CIRIA). (1993). *The design and construction of sheet-piled cofferdams*. CIRIA Special Publication 95.

Construction Industry Research and Information Association (CIRIA). (1994). *Value by competition — a guide to the competitive procurement of consultancy services for construction*. CIRIA Special Publication 117.

Construction Industry Research and Information Association (CIRIA). (1996a). *Control of risk: a guide to the systematic management of risk from construction*. CIRIA Special Publication 125.

Construction Industry Research and Information Association (CIRIA). (1996b). *Beach management manual*. CIRIA Report 153.

Construction Industry Research and Information Association (CIRIA). (1998). *Selecting contractors by value*. CIRIA Special Publication 150.

Construction Industry Research and Information Association (CIRIA). (2000). *A strategic framework for risk management*. Funders Report/CP/89.

Edwards, L. (1995). *Practical risk management in the construction industry*. Thomas Telford, London.

Efficiency Unit, Cabinet Office. (1995). *Construction procurement by Government. An Efficiency Unit Scrutiny*. HMSO, London.

European Construction Institute (ECI). (1997). *Partnering in the public sector — a toolkit for the implementation of post award, project specific partnering on construction profits*. ECI, Loughborough.

Environment Agency. (1997a). *Risk assessment and management (guidance for the assessment and management of risks in project management for engineering works)*. Engineering Project Management Group, Environment Agency.

Environment Agency. (1997b). *Benchmarking and scoping study of hydraulic river models*. Environment Agency, Technical Report W88.

European Commission Directive 93/67/EEC. *Risk of notified substances*.

Farraday, R. V. and Charlton, F. G. (1983). *Hydraulic factors in bridge design*. Thomas Telford, London.

Goda, Y. (1985). *Random seas and design of maritime structures*. University of Tokyo Press, Tokyo.

Graff, J. (1981). An investigation of the frequency distribution of annual sea level at ports around Great Britain. *Estuarine, Coastal and Shelf Science*, **12**, No.4, April, 389–449.

Higgs, A. W., Campbell, G. G. and Dunn, P. J. (1998). Reconstruction of Bray Weir on the River Thames. *Water & Environmental Management J.*, **12**, April, No.2.

HM Treasury. (1997a). *Guidance Document No. 1, Essential requirements for construction procurement*. Treasury Public Enquiry Unit.

HM Treasury. (1997b). *Guidance Document No. 2, Value for money in construction procurement*. Treasury Public Enquiry Unit.

HM Treasury. (1997c). *Guidance Document No. 3, Appointment of consultants and contractors*. Treasury Public Enquiry Unit.

HM Treasury. (1999a). *Guidance Document No. 4, Teamworking, partnering and incentives*. Treasury Public Enquiry Unit.

HM Treasury. (1999b). *Guidance Document No. 5, Procurement strategies*. Treasury Public Enquiry Unit.

HM Treasury. (1999c). *Guidance Document No. 6, Financial aspects of projects.* Treasury Public Enquiry Unit.

HR Wallingford. (1995). *A catalogue of synthetic wave data around the coast of England and Wales.* Ramsey, D.L. and Harford, C.M. Report SR 373, Nov. 1995.

HR Wallingford. (1996a). *Wave forces on vertical and composite breakwaters.* Report SR443, March 1996.

HR Wallingford. (1996b). *Reservoir dams: wave conditions, wave overtopping and slab protection.* HR Wallingford/DETR Report SR 459.

HR Wallingford. (1998). *A catalogue of instrumentally measured wave data around the coast of England and Wales.* Harford, C.M. Report TR51, Oct. 1998.

HR Wallingford. (1999a). *Forces on vertical breakwaters: effects of oblique or short vertical waves.* Report SR 465, March 1999.

HR Wallingford. (1999b). *River diversions — design guide.* Report SR 558, 1999.

Latham, M. (1994). *Constructing the team.* HMSO, London.

Institute of Hydrology. (1998). *Hydrological Data, UK (Hydrometric register and statistics).* The Institute of Hydrology, Wallingford.

Institute of Hydrology. (2000). *Flood estimation handbook.* Five volumes. Institute of Hydrology, Wallingford.

Institution of Civil Engineers. (1995). *The engineering and construction contract, 2nd edition.* Thomas Telford, London.

Institution of Civil Engineers. (1998). *The professional services contract, 2nd edition.* Thomas Telford, London.

Institution of Civil Engineers and the Faculty and Institute of Actuaries. (1998). *Risk analysis and management for projects.* Thomas Telford, London.

Insurance Institute of London. (1985). *Construction and erection insurance report.* Advanced Study Group, No. 208A, May 1985.

Ministry of Agriculture, Fisheries and Food (MAFF). (1993). *Project Appraisal Guidance Notes Report PN1471.* MAFF, London.

NERC. (1975). *Flood studies report.* Five volumes.

Proudman Oceanographic Laboratory (POL). (1997). *Spatial analyses for the UK coast.* Internal Document No. 112. Proudman Oceanographic Laboratory, June 1997.

Saul, R. and Svensson, H. (1982). *On the theory of ship collision against bridge piers.* International Association for Bridge and Structural Engineering (IABSE).

Simm. J. and Cruickshank, I. (1998). *Construction risk in coastal engineering.* Thomas Telford, London.

Whitehouse, R. J. S. (1998). *Scour at marine structures — A manual for practical applications.* Thomas Telford, London.

Wilson. E. M. (1990). *Engineering hydrology.* 4th edition. MacMillan.

Appendices

Appendix 1.
Actions to be undertaken at each step in the risk identification, assessment and management process

---

STEP 1   Strategic level risk assessments

Before entering into a detailed project risk assessment it is important to recognise that higher strategic business assessments will also be necessary. These should address:

- Establishing the overall business objectives and the business risks that could impact on the achievement of these objectives.
- Whether these business objectives are met or will be compromised by entering into the project.

Once this step is undertaken then steps 2 to 11 can proceed. This guide focuses on construction risk and further guidance on strategic business assessments can be found in CIRIA (1996a).

STEP 2   Identify all project objectives and an appropriate level of detail for a risk assessment

The aims and objectives of the project or contract should be agreed and then ordered into a hierarchy. The objectives will depend upon which organisation is undertaking the assessment and on the project stage. For instance, the insurer may only be interested in the risks that they are being asked to insure whereas the client will be interested in whole-life risks of the project.

The objective should identify which (possibly all) of the following risk types are to be considered in the assessment:

- cost
- time
- quality
- environment
- safety.

For each risk type, the risk manager should specify the performance indicator. These may include:

- targets, which need to be met and require actions to be implemented
- minimise/maximise objectives, for example to minimise cost
- risk-based indicators, for example, a client may require completion on time with a 90% probability while a contractor may wish to make the probability of severe flood damage remote.

STEP 2 continued

An appropriate level of detail for the management process should also be established at this stage, depending upon the risks involved. For instance, it would be inappropriate for the client to employ detailed computational-modelling techniques to predict risk conditions for a low-value river-wall maintenance contract. In this case it would perhaps be more appropriate to carry out a short desk-assessment to identify the risks and mitigation measures.

STEP 3   Identify hazards and risks

Unless the hazards or risks are identified, they cannot be consciously managed. It is therefore crucial to spend time identifying threats to project objectives and to present them in a form that assists with their control. The questions that *always* have to be addressed are:

- What can go wrong?
- What can jeopardise achieving the project/contract objectives?

Methods which make this process effective are presented in CIRIA (1996a) and include:

- what can go wrong analysis
- free and structured brainstorming
- prompt lists/check lists (see Appendix 5)
- structured interviews/risk workshops
- hindsight reviews and case studies.

The outcome of the risk-identification process is commonly presented as an initial risk register or portfolio. This is a concise logical-description of the risks, organised by type, origin and with the appropriate details given for each risk. The development of the risk register is a continual process throughout the project. The risk register allows management to clarify issues as they arise and reach sound conclusions.

An example of this is detailed under Section 2 of Appendix 2.

STEP 4   Consider the ownership of the risks

Identify ownership of the risks. The owner of the risk should be defined by the contract. If the assessment is undertaken prior to the preparation of the contract conditions, then consideration should be given to whether the contract satisfactorily shares the risk. If it is being undertaken at a later stage, consideration should be given to whom the risk has been apportioned.

An example of this is shown in Section 2 of Appendix 2.

STEP 5   Assess the likelihood and consequences of these hazards

The next step is to establish the likelihood and consequence of the hazards. There are many types of risk-assessment procedure. These range from generic, semi-quantitative procedures, that assign approximate likelihood and consequences to pre-defined risks, through to statistical modelling and scenario modelling that may be used to estimate probabilistic outcomes of various project indicators.

Some of these methods are detailed in Section 1.2 of Appendix 2 with examples shown in Tables A2.1 to A2.5.

STEP 6   Identify control/mitigation measures

Actions to control/minimise the impact of risks are usually referred to as risk-mitigation measures. If the hazard (risk source) is understood, together with the circumstances leading to its consequence and likelihood, mitigation measures can more easily be identified using similar techniques to those used initially to identify risks. Mitigation measures are normally added to the risk register. Some hazards, such as lack of communication or incompatibility of systems, defy assessment in quantitative terms, but cannot be dismissed. Even if the impact of risk is difficult to estimate, the identification of effective mitigation measures can still be very important.

The benefit of risk mitigation is a reduction in either the consequence or the likelihood of adverse outcomes, or both. The residual risks can be identified by assessing the change effected to the original risks and the resulting impacts. Secondary risks (i.e. those that are caused by the mitigation action) can be a problem and need to be taken into account when considering the residual risks.

Each mitigation option can often be used to control a variety of risks (so the accumulated benefits of mitigation should be compared with the cost of implementation, not forgetting the value of benefits that cannot be assessed in quantitative terms).

Accountability for the mitigation actions should be identified, including a review of its feasibility and establishment of an implementation plan if required.

Guidance on risk mitigation and control strategies may be found in Section 2.5 in Chapter 2. Examples of control measures may be found in Tables 2.2, A2.7 and A2.8, columns 7, 8 and 9 under Chapter 2 and Appendix 2 respectively.

STEP 7   Assess residual risks (including new 'secondary' risks created by any mitigation measures)

The mitigation measures identified are likely to reduce the primary risk but will leave 'residual risks' and or create new ones. These risks should be adequately assessed.

For instance, introduction of a cofferdam at the front of a retaining wall to remove the risk of a concrete pour being stopped due to high river flows will have a residual risk that water will overtop the cofferdam and still flood the works. It may also introduce new health and safety risks of having to work in a confined space.

Examples of the assessment of the residual risks may be found in Tables 2.2, A2.7 and A2.8, columns 10, 11 and 12 under Chapter 2 and Appendix 2.

STEP 8   Estimate the cost of mitigation measures

Any mitigation measures are likely to have cost implications. These costs should be evaluated and noted in the register in preparation for an assessment of benefit gained from the additional cost.

See column 12 of Tables 2.2, A2.7 and A2.8 under Chapter 2 and Appendix 2.

STEP 9   Estimate the benefit of mitigation measures

There is little point in introducing a mitigation measure if the cost of doing so vastly exceeds the benefit gained from it. It is therefore advisable to evaluate this benefit wherever possible and as early in the project as possible. This may be difficult when considering issues such as safety and the environment.

For instance, using the example above, the construction of a cofferdam is likely to be expensive and, while thought essential to prevent say the delay of five concrete pours over the duration of the works, the cofferdam may not prove to be cost effective.

Column 12 of Tables 2.2, A2.7 and A2.8 (Chapter 2 and Appendix 2) shows an example of this.

STEP 10   Select and implement beneficial mitigation actions

Unfortunately, this step is often forgotten and good ideas to limit risks are often not fully implemented. The risk register should be linked to an action plan which details the mitigation measures and when they should be put into force. Measures may be proactive or reactive, depending upon the risk, and are probably best broken into the separate project stages.

An example of part of an action plan for a contractor is given below (based on Tables A2.7 to A2.9 in Appendix 2):

Pre award:
- Recommend to client that they undertake to drive additional boreholes at Ch 60–90 m.
- Recommend to client to carry out additional sediment analysis for contaminated dredged material.
- Etc.

On award:
- Confirm commencement date with dredging subcontractor.
- Etc.

During contract:
- Warn personnel regarding possibility of finding ordnance.
- Etc.

On low flows:
- Monitor to determine whether dredger will be able to gain access to the site.
- Etc.

On receipt of flood warning:
- Check if additional anchors are required for the dredger.
- Etc.

STEP 11   Monitor and review the process/feedback into the cycle

The risk register should continually evolve with the project. Reviewing previous events provides a further insight into the risks involved and their interaction. Risks should be reviewed at appropriate times throughout the construction phase with additional reviews at particular milestones, or if a major event occurs. Knowledge gained during the review should be fed back into the risk assessment process.

Once the project has been completed, the risks no longer exist for that project. However, to improve the approach to risk management for future projects, the lessons learnt should be properly debated and documented. The risk management approach should therefore become progressively more effective for subsequent projects. Continual improvements should result as risk management integrates naturally into the management structure.

Appendix 2.
Other risk assessment and modelling methods

This appendix provides an overview of the various additional risk assessment and modelling methods referred to in Chapter 2 which are additional to those described in Sections 2.8 and 2.9. The methods are described along with references for further reading should the user wish to investigate the approaches in greater depth.

Note that while the majority of the examples shown in this appendix are based on 'cost risk', it should be recognised that the same process could be applied to time, safety or even environmental risk assessments. The following examples are not exhaustive, and other methods and forms of presentation may be more appropriate for any specific case. Remember that the tools and techniques should only be used if it is worthwhile to do so.

A2.1. SCHEMATIC/DIAGRAMMATIC METHODS

A2.1.1. Influence diagrams and rich pictures

Influence diagrams can be used to illustrate both the various influences on risks and how the risks relate to one another. They can be used to promote brainstorming and lead to an increased understanding of the dependencies and priorities involved in a project. Assuming that all risks for a project are independent can be misleading.

Figure A2.1 shows how links between risks can be demonstrated through an influence diagram. Some software packages combine influence diagrams and Monte Carlo simulations to produce very effective models.

Rich pictures can be used to illustrate how the various components of a project fit together in terms of the project process and the human elements that can affect decisions. The 'picture' may comprise any information in any format. For example, a mix of photos, diagrams, tables and notes with links between each shown. The intention is that the picture provides an overview of key issues for the project and as a risk-management tool, they are a useful starting point for the identification of risks to a project.

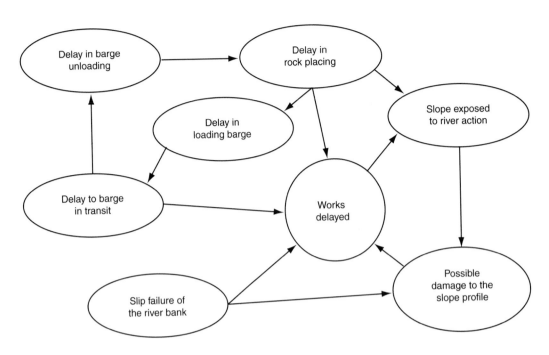

Figure A2.1.   Influence diagram for the construction of river bank protection

A2.1.2. Likelihood — consequence tables

A key element in assessing the significance of a risk is to estimate its likelihood and the consequences should the risk arise.

CIRIA (1996a) gives typical guidelines for assessing risks in this way. Likelihood is classified into five classes from 'frequent' to 'improbable' and consequence similarly classified from 'catastrophic' to 'negligible'. For both likelihood and consequence, quantitative indicators for probability and cost are also given. This allows risk-cost or risk-acceptability to be assessed, based on the combination of likelihood and consequence. This approach is designed as a coarse but easily applied method to assess and compare risks. Special consideration should be given to catastrophic events.

Extracts from the classes given in CIRIA (1996a) are given in Tables A2.1 to A2.5. Tables A2.1 and A2.2 define the description/scoring for probability and consequence. Tables A2.3 to A2.5 present the risk in terms of importance (i.e. simple score), cost and acceptability.

Note that care is needed when combining likelihood and consequences to take account of the importance of the risk. Although the product of likelihood and consequence gives the mean impact of risk, in many cases the variance can be very significant. Typically, high consequence, low-likelihood risks will be more important to manage than low-consequence high-likelihood risks even though they have the same expected risk impact.

Table A2.1. Typical scales for likelihood/probability

Description	Guidance	Scale	Probability
Frequent	Likely to occur frequently many times during the period of concern (e.g. project duration, life of the structure)	4	$100/T$
Probable	Several times in the period of concern	3	$10/T$
Occasional	Some time in the period of concern	2	$1/T$
Remote	Unlikely but possible in the period of concern (e.g. once in ten times the life of the structure)	1	$1/10T$
Improbable	So unlikely that it can be assumed that it will not occur or it cannot occur	0	$1/100T$

Note: T = period of time over which the likelihood/probability of risk is being assessed

Table A2.2. Typical scales for consequence

Description	Guidance	Scale	Cost
Catastrophic	Death, system loss, criminal guilt, bankruptcy	4	£$100V$
Critical	Occupation threatening injury or illness, major damage, substantial damages, exceeds contingency, dividend at risk	3	£$10V$
Serious	Lost time injury or illness, damage causing down time of plant, consumes contingency, requires an insurance claim, project delays	2	£V
Marginal	Injury or illness requiring first aid at work only, minor damage that can await routine maintenance, will only require an apology letter, accommodated as part of contingency or insurance excess	1	£$V/10$
Negligible	So minor as to be regarded as without consequence	0	£$V/100$

Note: £V = average value consequence

A2.1.3. Flow diagrams

Flow diagrams in this context contain a sequence of instructions for problem solving. The instructions are the steps in a task and the responses determine the route to be followed, and are often used as a prelude to computer programming or modelling, since they follow a logical path (see Figure A2.2). Flow diagrams

Table A2.3.   Assessment of risk importance

Likelihood	Consequence	Catastrophic	Critical	Serious	Marginal	Negligible
	Scale	(4)	(3)	(2)	(1)	(0)
Frequent	(4)	16	12	8	4	0
Probable	(3)	12	9	6	3	0
Occasional	(2)	8	6	4	2	0
Remote	(1)	4	3	2	1	0
Improbable	(0)	0	0	0	0	0

Table A2.4.   Assessment of risk cost

Likelihood	Consequence	Catastrophic	Critical	Serious	Marginal	Negligible
	Prob. Cost	£100V	£10V	£V	£V/10	£V/100
Frequent	100/T	10 000V/T	1000V/T	100V/T	10V/T	V/T
Probable	10/T	1000V/T	100V/T	10V/T	V/T	V/10T
Occasional	1/T	100V/T	10V/T	V/T	V/10T	V/100T
Remote	1/10T	10V/T	V/T	V/10T	V/100T	V/1000T
Improbable	1/100T	V/T	V/10T	V/100T	V/1000T	V/10 000T

Table A2.5.   Assessment of risk acceptability

Likelihood	Consequence				
	Catastrophic	Critical	Serious	Marginal	Negligible
Frequent	Unacceptable	Unacceptable	Unacceptable	Undesirable	Undesirable
Probable	Unacceptable	Unacceptable	Undesirable	Undesirable	Acceptable
Occasional	Unacceptable	Undesirable	Undesirable	Acceptable	Acceptable
Remote	Undesirable	Undesirable	Acceptable	Acceptable	Negligible
Improbable	Undesirable	Acceptable	Acceptable	Negligible	Negligible

Key:	Description	Guidance
	Unacceptable	Intolerable, must be eliminated, transferred (if possible)
	Undesirable	To be avoided if reasonably practicable, detailed investigation and cost/programme benefit justification required, top level approval needed, monitoring essential
	Acceptable	Can be accepted provided the risk is managed
	Negligible	No further consideration needed

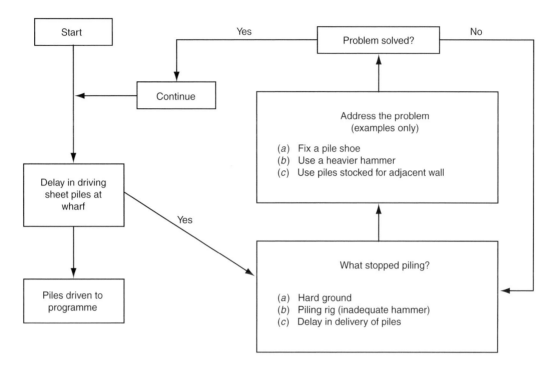

Figure A2.2.   A simple flow diagram

can be used to show causes, consequences, independent events, and the mitigating effects of decisions that are implemented.

A2.1.4. Decision event trees

A decision tree extends the concept of a flow diagram by allowing input of quantities (i.e. likelihood and consequence) into the decision-making process. A decision tree is a diagrammatic representation of a set of possible alternatives in the form of a network. The network shows the alternative paths available to the decision-maker. Therefore, it illustrates the sequence of decisions and the expected outcomes under each set of circumstances.

In addition, decision trees can include events that are beyond direct control, such as the occurrence of storms. Combining decisions and events enables comprehensive assessment of risk arising from different decisions. The risk can be quantified, if likelihood and consequence are also quantified in some way. This leads to an assessment of the Expected Monetary Value (EMV) arising from each set of decisions. Comparison of the cost arising from making certain decisions can then be input into the decision-making process.

By adopting an analytical approach such as a decision tree, the decision-maker recognises the existence of certain basic elements of risk and their consequence. The use of a decision tree gives a structured approach to setting out a risk strategy and a quantified indication of the consequences.

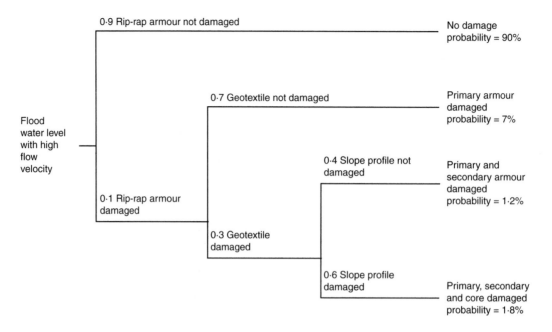

Figure A2.3.   An example event tree showing the possible impact of high river flows at a site just prior to issue of the completion certificate

The reverse of this concept is a fault tree, which describes the logical combination of causes leading to a particular failure. This useful tool can help the decision-maker to back analyse a decision tree and check that no major risks have been overlooked. An example of an event tree is shown in Figure A2.3.

A2.1.5. Risk calendars

Risk calendars are based on the project programme and illustrate where in the programme the risks fall. This enables the project manager to see at a glance the levels of risk in a particular section of the project. The distribution over time of the risk levels in each section of the project can be shown as a bar chart against the actual activity (see Figure A2.4).

A2.2.   RECORDING RISKS AND CONTROL STRATEGIES

A2.2.1. Risk registers

The successful identification and control of risk is underpinned by the systematic assessment and recording of risk items and mitigation measures. Risk registers offer a simple method for recording and presenting risk information. The complexity of a risk register may be altered to suit the needs of a particular job or preferences of the person undertaking the assessment, however the

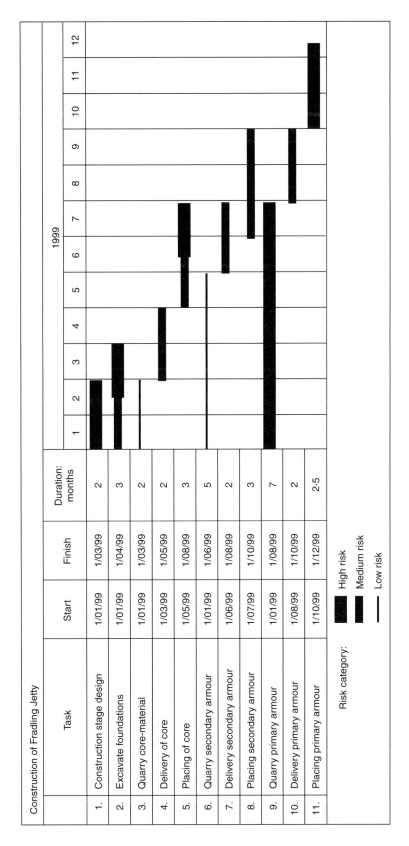

Figure A2.4. A simple risk calendar

fundamental approach remains consistent. The following Tables A2.6 to A2.8 show a register created using a risk judgement approach (Table A2.6), a register created using descriptive methods of assessment (Table A2.7) and a register with assessment of risk importance (Table A2.8).

Table 2.2 in Chapter 2 is a development of the above showing a register with assessment of risk cost.

Note that further examples of registers using more complex methods of risk assessment are given in Section 3 below.

A2.2.2. Strategy summary

A useful method of recording risk control strategies was put forward by Edwards (1995) where risks are set against the control strategies in a simple table. This simple method (see example in Table A2.9) is useful as one can see at a glance:

- that all risks are being controlled
- exactly how the risk is being controlled
- if too many risks are being controlled under one tactic (e.g. too many risks being put against the contingency fund).

A2.3. COST AND PROBABILISTIC METHODS

In addition to those methods already presented in Chapter 2 (Section 2.8), there are a range of other cost risk-assessment methods which may be considered. These are presented in the following sections.

A2.3.1. Percentage/lump sum to tender value (CPM1 in Table 2.5 of Chapter 2)

This method is the simplest form of risk assessment that can be undertaken. It relies entirely upon engineering judgement and simply entails adding a lump-sum cost (or contingency) to allow for 'risks'. For example, a contractor may add a fixed sum and an additional time period to the work programme, to allow for 'risks'.

A2.3.2. Risk register with percentage/lump sum per item (CPM2 in Table 2.5 of Chapter 2)

This method again relies heavily upon engineering judgement, but the risk is sub-divided into separate elements allowing evaluation to be more focused. An example of this method is shown in Table A2.6 of Section A2.2.1 above.

Table A2.6. Partially completed risk register using a judgement approach

	Initial risk				Mitigation			
Column 1	*Column 2*	*Column 3*	*Column 6*	*Column 7*	*Column 8*	*Column 9*	*Column 13*
Element	Risk	Owner	Assessment	Mitigation measure	Mitigation by whom	Mitigation when	Cost of mitigation/ comment
Drive sheet piled wall from pontoon	Piles not arrived on site	Contractor	£1000	Pre-order (providing time float)	Contractor	On award	None
	High river flows preventing positioning/ driving	Contractor	£800	Use additional anchors if required	Contractor	On receipt of flood warning	£350
	Hard ground conditions/ obstructions	Client	£6000	Drive additional boreholes at Ch 60–90 m	Client	Pre-award	£6000
	Etc.						

Table A2.6. *continued*

Column 1	Column 2	Initial risk				Mitigation			
		Column 3	Column 6	Column 7	Column 8	Column 9	Column 13
Element	Risk	Owner	Assessment	Mitigation measure	Mitigation by whom	Mitigation when	Cost of mitigation/ comment
Dredge in front of new wall	Dredger not available	Contractor/ Subcontractor	£1000	Confirm start date	Contractor	On award	None
	Low river flows preventing access	Contractor	£200	Use land-based plant if required	Contractor	Monitor when flows reduce	None as already on site (note possible new risk of plant sinking into river bed)
	Contaminated sediments	Client	£7000	Carry out additional sediment analysis	Client	Pre-award	£500
	Ordnance found	Contractor	£3000	Carry out magnetometer surveys and warn personnel/place in H&S Plan	Contractor	On award and during contract	£450
Etc.							

Table A2.7. *Part of a completed risk register or portfolio with descriptive methods of assessment*

	Initial risk						Mitigation					
Column 1	Column 2	Column 3	Column 4	Column 5	Column 6	Column 7	Column 8	Column 9	Column 10	Column 11	Column 12	Column 13
Element	Risk	Owner	Likelihood	Con-sequences	Assessment	Mitigation measure	Mitigation by whom	Mitigation when	Revised likelihood	Revised con-sequences	Revised assessment	Cost of mitigation/comment
Drive sheet piled wall from marine pontoon	Piles not arrived on site	Contractor	Occasional	Serious	Undesirable	Pre-order (providing time float)	Contractor	On award	Remote	Serious	Acceptable	None
	High river flows preventing position-ing/driving	Contractor	Remote	Marginal	Acceptable	Use additional anchors if required	Contractor	On receipt of flood warning	Remote	Marginal	Acceptable	£350
	Hard ground conditions/ obstructions	Client	Occasional	Serious	Undesirable	Drive additional boreholes at Ch 60–90 m	Client	Pre-award	Remote	Serious	Acceptable	£6000
	Etc.											

Table A2.7. continued

			Initial risk			Mitigation						
Column 1	Column 2	Column 3	Column 4	Column 5	Column 6	Column 7	Column 8	Column 9	Column 10	Column 11	Column 12	Column 13
Element	Risk	Owner	Likelihood	Con-sequences	Assessment	Mitigation measure	Mitigation by whom	Mitigation when	Revised likelihood	Revised con-sequences	Revised assessment	Cost of mitigation/comment
Dredge in front of new wall	Dredger not available	Contractor/Sub-contractor	Remote	Serious	Acceptable	Confirm start date	Contractor	On award	Improbable	Serious	Acceptable	None
	Low river flows preventing access	Contractor	Improbable	Marginal	Negligible	Use land-based plant if required	Contractor	Monitor when flows reduce	Improbable	Negligible	Negligible	None as already on site (note possible new risk of plant sinking into river bed)
	Con-taminated sediments	Client	Probable	Serious	Undesirable	Carry out additional sediment analysis	Client	Pre-award	Remote	Serious	Negligible	£500
	Ordnance found	Contractor	Occasional	Catastro-phic	Unacceptable	Carry out magneto-meter surveys and warn personnel/place in H&S Plan	Contractor	On award and during contract	Improbable	Serious	Acceptable	£450
Etc.												

Table A2.8. Part of a completed risk register or portfolio with assessment of risk importance

| | | | Initial risk | | | | | Mitigation | | | | | |
Column 1	Column 2	Column 3	Column 4	Column 5	Column 6	Column 7	Column 8	Column 9	Column 10	Column 11	Column 12	Column 13
Element	Risk	Owner	Likelihood	Con-sequences	Assessment	Mitigation measure	Mitigation by whom	Mitigation when	Revised likelihood	Revised con-sequences	Revised assessment	Cost of mitigation/comment
Drive sheet piled wall from marine pontoon	Piles not arrived on site	Contractor	2	2	4	Pre-order providing time float	Contractor	On award	1	2	2	None
	High river flows preventing position-ing/driving	Contractor	1	1	2	Use additional anchors if required	Contractor	On receipt of flood warning	1	1	1	£350
	Hard ground conditions/obstructions	Client	2	2	4	Drive additional boreholes at Ch 60–90 m	Client	Pre-award	1	2	2	£6000
	Etc.											

Table A2.8.   continued

	Column 1	Column 2	Column 3	Initial risk			Mitigation						
				Column 4	Column 5	Column 6	Column 7	Column 8	Column 9	Column 10	Column 11	Column 12	Column 13
	Element	Risk	Owner	Likelihood	Con-sequences	Assessment	Mitigation measure	Mitigation by whom	Mitigation when	Revised likelihood	Revised con-sequences	Revised assessment	Cost of mitigation/comment
	Dredge in front of new wall	Dredger not available	Contractor/Sub-contractor	1	2	2	Confirm start date	Contractor	On award	0	2	0	None
		Low river flows preventing access	Contractor	0	1	0	Use land-based plant if required	Contractor	Monitor when flows reduce	0	1	0	None as already on site
		Con-taminated sediments	Client	3	2	6	Carry out additional sediment analysis	Client	Pre-award	1	2	2	£500
		Ordnance found	Contractor	2	4	6	Carry out magnet-ometer surveys and warn personnel/place in H&S Plan	Contractor	On award and during contract	0	4	0	£450
	Etc.												

Table A2.9. Record of risk control strategies

Risk	Tactic to offset								
	Contract conditions with client	Contract conditions with sub-contractor (the same as with the client)	Currencies of payments	Fixed price quotes	Insurance	Contingency fund	Construct sheltered berth	Pre order material/plant	. . . etc.
General									
Financial — insurance market					• (buy now)				
Economic — exchange rate			•		•	•			
Planning — permissions and approvals delay or rejections, policy and practice change rights of way	•								
Etc.									
Project									
Ground related issues — obstacles and hard ground	•	•				•			
Ground related issues — variation in founding levels	•	•				•			
Piles — reliability of supply	•	•					•	•	
Piles, coating	•	•						•	
Measurement method	•	•	•						
Restrictions on noise levels	•	•							
Restrictions on working hours	•	•							
Water-related issues — wave height	•	•			•		•		
Water-related issues — surge effects (+ve and −ve)	•	•			•				
Water-related issues — tidal water levels	•	•			•				
Water-related issues — high river currents	•	•			•		•		
Wind action (wind-speed)	•	•			•				
Etc.									

A2.3.3. Risk register with percentage/lump sum against a spread of risk probabilities per item) (CPM4 in Table 2.5 of Chapter 2)

This technique allows a more detailed assessment of the risk element by permitting a spread of risk to be assessed (see Table A2.9). In this example, an average risk allowance and a maximum risk allowance can be assessed. The method is relatively simple and has the benefit of recognising that the maximum costs should not be simply added together, since the likelihood of all maximum costs occurring on the same contract is extremely small.

The maximum likely risk condition may be calculated using the following:

$$\begin{aligned} \text{Maximum likely} \quad &= \quad \text{average risk} + \text{square root of summed risk-spread} \\ \text{risk condition} \quad &= \quad \pounds 19\,000 + (\pounds 55\,492\,500)^{0.5} \\ &= \quad \pounds 26\,449 \end{aligned}$$

This method is known as the 'root mean square' technique because of the calculation technique used.

In the example shown in Table A2.10, the maximum risk that could occur is £200 000 whereas the maximum likely risk is assessed as £26 449. The difference between these measures of risk will generally increase as a larger number of risks are considered.

A2.3.4. Total probability method (CPM6 in Table 2.5 in Chapter 2)

This is an alternative to Monte Carlo Simulation (MCS) (CPM7 in Table 2.5 in Chapter 2) which can be used where all of the risks are specified as discrete pairs of probability and consequence. The Total Probability Method (TPM) involves calculating all of the possible risk combinations, together with the associated combined probability. This leads to a probability distribution of risk similar to that obtained by MCS. The total probability of all combinations is 1·0.

The advantage of the TPM is that it is precise and therefore avoids the possibility of sampling error that may occur with MCS. While being relatively simple for a few cases, however, it can become quite complex with larger combinations of risks and risk categories. See Box A2.1 for a simple example of the TPM.

A2.4. COMPUTATIONAL RISK MODELS

Computational modelling offers the user the ability to examine both more and complex risks. The user should never forget, however, that the model can only perform to the quality of data supplied. All models will therefore be incorrect to

Table A2.10.   Part of a risk register or portfolio with assessment of risk cost using 'root mean square' method

| Column 1 | Column 2 | Column 3 | Column 4 | Initial risk | | | | | | Miti-gation |
				Column 5	Column 6 (Col. 4×Col. 5)	Column 7	Column 8 (Col. 4×Col. 7)	Column 9 (Col. 8 − Col. 6)	Column 10	Etc.
Element	Risk	Owner	Likelihood	Average con-sequences	Average risk allowance	Maximum con-sequences	Maximum risk allowance	Risk spread	Risk spread squared	
Drive sheet piled wall from marine pontoon	Piles not arrived on site	Contractor	10%	£10 000	£1000	£20 000	£2000	£1000	£1 000 000	
	High river flows preventing positioning/ driving	Contractor	5%	£20 000	£1000	£25 000	£1250	£250	£202 500	
	Hard ground conditions/ obstructions	Client	20%	£30 000	£6000	£40 000	£8000	£2000	£4 000 000	
Etc.										

Table A2.10. continued

				Initial risk						Miti-gation
Column 1	*Column 2*	*Column 3*	*Column 4*	*Column 5*	*Column 6* (Col. 4 × Col. 5)	*Column 7*	*Column 8* (Col. 4 × Col. 7)	*Column 9* (Col. 8 − Col. 6)	*Column 10*	*Etc.*
Element	Risk	Owner	Likelihood	Average con-sequences	Average risk allowance	Maximum con-sequences	Maximum risk allowance	Risk spread	Risk spread squared	
Dredge in front of new wall	Dredger not available	Contractor/sub-contractor	10%	£10 000	£1000	£15 000	£1500	£500	£250 000	
	Low river flows preventing access	Contractor	2%	£10 000	£200	£20 000	£400	£200	£40 000	
	Con-taminated sediments	Client	35%	£20 000	£7000	£40 000	£14 000	£7000	£49 000 000	
	Ordnance found	Contractor	10%	£30 000	£3000	£40 000	£4000	£1000	£1 000 000	
	Etc.									
Totals					£19 000	£200 000			£55 492 500	

Maximum likely risk condition = average risk + square root of the summed risk-spread
$$= £19\,000 + (£55\,492\,500)^{0.5}$$
$$= £26\,449$$

Box A2.1. Simple example of the Total Probability Method

Consider the analysis of two risks only, say, the potential change in estuary bed-level and the discovery of ordnance within the channel. The probability of occurrence, consequence and hence risk of each individual event has been estimated. For example, see Table A2.11.

Table A2.11. Summary of event risks

Item	Risk	Probability	Consequence	Risk value
Ordnance found	None	75%	£0	£0
	Marginal	20%	£20 000	£4000
	Severe	5%	£40 000	£2000
Change in bed level	None	85%	£0	£0
	Marginal	10%	£30 000	£3000
	Severe	5%	£40 000	£2000

A matrix of combined probabilities and costs may then be calculated, as shown in Table A2.12.

Table A2.12. Combined probabilities and costs

(Combined probability is the product of the separate probabilities)		Degree of change in bed level		
		None (0·85)	Marginal (0·10)	Severe (0·05)
Ordnance found in river bed	None (0·75)	0·6375	0·0750	0·0375
	Marginal (0·20)	0·1700	0·0200	0·0100
	Severe (0·05)	0·0425	0·0050	0·0025

(Combined cost is the sum of the separate costs)		Degree of change in bed level		
		None	Marginal	Severe
Ordnance found in river bed	None	£0	£30 000	£40 000
	Marginal	£20 000	£50 000	£60 000
	Severe	£40 000	£70 000	£80 000

The information from these two tables may then be ordered by cost and used to plot a simple probability distribution, as shown in Table A2.13 and Figure A2.5.

Box A2.1. continued

Table A2.13. Probability distribution of costs

Cost	Probability of cost	Probability of matching or exceeding cost
£0	0·6375	1·0
£20 000	0·1700	
£30 000	0·0750	
£40 000	0·0800*	
£50 000	0·0200	
£60 000	0·0100	
£70 000	0·0050	
£80 000	0·0025	

* 0·0800 = 0·0425 + 0·0375

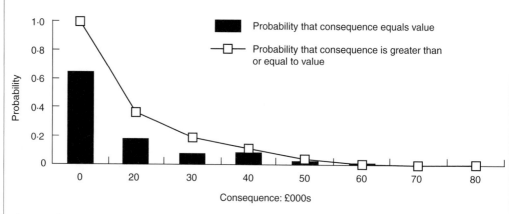

Figure A2.5. Cost probability distribution

It can be seen that the likelihood of incurring no cost is 0·64. The probability of matching or exceeding this 'no cost' is logically 1. The likelihood of incurring a cost of £40 000 is 0·08 (1 in 12) and of matching or exceeding £40 000, about 0·12 (1 in 8). Alternatively, one could establish that there is a 96% probability that costs will not exceed £50 000.

some extent since it is impossible to measure all possible hazards and their impacts.

Four techniques are briefly outlined in the following paragraphs. Further details, along with some case studies, may be found in the 'sister' guide, *Construction risk in coastal engineering* (Simm and Cruickshank, 1998). *Construction risk in coastal engineering* preceded production of this guide by one year and was compiled with contributions made by a different steering group. The coastal manual covers similar topics, but for the coastal environment, and generally in greater depth.

Cost-risk techniques

A cost-risk model resembles a normal schedule of quantities and rates and can be implemented on a spreadsheet using the same structure as an ordinary project cost-table. The difference is that the cost-risk model includes information about uncertainty in cost rates and quantities, as well as the work items discussed in earlier sections.

The uncertainties can be specified by simple probability distributions — in many cases the triangular distribution (minimum, most likely, maximum) is as sophisticated as can be justified.

Schedule-risk techniques

Schedule risk represents the progress of a project in time and is used to estimate the probability profile of the completion time and any project milestones. Schedule risk can incorporate a number of uncertainties, such as:

- rate of progress of activities
- quantities
- impact of weather on rate of progress
- damage due to severe weather, with subsequent repair times
- failure to meet tidal windows
- impact of specific delays on overall project progress.

Schedule planning is conventionally based on activity networks. These show the relationships between all of the activities in the project as well as start and finish dates and task duration. Critical path management (CPM) is based on a graphical project model defined as a network.

Modelling schedule-risk may be carried out using standard scheduling software (e.g. MS-Project) linked with a spreadsheet Monte Carlo sampling program (e.g. @Risk).

Scenario modelling

Scenario modelling aims to represent the possible future course of events. Scenario modelling can track progress and simulate decision making at a fine level of detail, whereas schedule modelling has difficulty in dealing with events or decisions that take place during, and which affect, an activity.

The basis of a scenario model is to simulate the construction activities at regular time intervals (e.g. one day or one week). The model keeps track of rates of progress for all activities and percentage completion of the works. Hazards, such as floods or accidents, may be incorporated. The model may be run repeatedly during the project to provide a forecast of likely or possible completion conditions and may be used for decision support to consider 'what if' scenarios.

Real-time modelling

It is possible to update a scenario model as the project proceeds, to reduce the uncertainty in the final outcome. The uncertainty is progressively decreased as the project proceeds. Furthermore, the impact of decisions, which depend on the current status of the project, can be modelled in more detail if the model is updated to reflect the true progress.

Appendix 3.
Example of a risk management workshop

A3.1. INTRODUCTION

An example of a risk workshop is given in the following pages to illustrate how such a workshop may be conducted. A fictitious study, based on a true construction project, was invented for the purposes of the workshop. The text is written in the format of a workshop report and aims to summarise what occurred at the workshop as well as the agreed actions.

Note that Annex 2 of this appendix gives details of a typical agenda and blank forms for use in a risk workshop.

A3.2. AN OVERVIEW OF A RISK MANAGEMENT WORKSHOP

The various stages in a risk management workshop may be broadly defined as follows:

(*a*) Introductions
(*b*) Agree aims and objectives of the workshop
(*c*) Agree aims and objectives of the project
(*d*) Prioritise project objectives
(*e*) Identify project risks:

    (i) long list
    (ii) short list
    (iii)prioritise
    (iv)consolidate

(*f*) Generate risk portfolio
(*g*) Follow up tasks such as the development of:

    (i) cost plan
    (ii) risk calendar
    (iii)project contingencies
    (iv)risk register

The workshop presented in the following pages works through each of these stages, except for the follow up tasks. Since the example project was based around a real construction project three different sets of conclusions are presented for comparison. These are:

(a) The participants initial 'gut feel' for the project — prior to the risk workshop.
(b) Conclusions drawn from the risk workshop.
(c) Key issues that were identified or arose during the real construction project.

The following text is now presented in the form of a risk workshop report.

Replacement weir at Low Fradling

Risk management workshop

7 December 1998

1.   INTRODUCTION

A risk workshop was held on 7th December 1998 at the Low Fradling Project Office to assess the risks associated with the replacement of an ageing weir on the River Frad near Low Fradling. This report is based upon the discussions and findings made at the workshop.

2.   THE RISK MANAGEMENT WORKSHOP

The workshop was attended by client representatives, a prospective contractor and the designer, and was facilitated by Risk Consultant representatives. The attendees are listed below:

Client	Project Manager
Client	Operations Manager
Designer	Project Manager
Designer	Deputy Project Manager
Contractor	Regional Manager
Contractor	Estimator
Risk Consultant	Facilitator
Risk Consultant	Recorder

3.   WORKSHOP INTRODUCTIONS

The workshop
A brief introduction to risk management and the risk management workshop process was given by an independent facilitator.

The project
The designer's project manager gave a brief introduction to the project. Details of the project may be found under Annex 1 of this report.

4.   PROJECT AND WORKSHOP AIMS AND OBJECTIVES

The aims and objectives of both the workshop and the project were first agreed. The aims provide the structure in which to expand, develop and focus the workshop, while the objectives are the measurable goals that, if met, achieve these aims. The objectives therefore provide the framework within which the risks to the project are judged. If a risk does not impact on the objectives then it is not a risk to the project. It is vital that the objectives are measurable, clear, meaningful and understood by the whole of the workshop. This can be summarised by the acronym SMART:

Simple
Measurable
Achievable
Realistic
Time bound

The main aim of the workshop was to assess the risks associated with the replacement of an ageing weir on the River Frad at Low Fradling. This workshop aims to concentrate solely on construction risks rather than more general project risks. Full details of the proposed construction project may be found in Annex 1.

Aim of the project
To replace the ageing weir at Low Fradling.

Project objectives
The following objectives were identified, discussed and agreed by the workshop:

- Time

  - To be completed by April 2000 if possible
  - Must be completed by September 2000 at the latest

- Cost

  - To cost less than £4 million to fit with the client's budget
  - To ensure an early warning system to identify lowest out-turn cost

- Quality

  - Accuracy of tolerances on critical items

- Safety

  - Better than industry norms for accidents

- Environmental

  - Public access maintained
  - Noise limits 8 a.m. to 6 p.m., and different limits for 6 p.m. to 8 a.m.

- Communications

  - Ensure monthly and event-based external communications through a series of meetings and newsletters as appropriate.

A simple ranking exercise was undertaken by the group to assess the agreed objectives against each other and to identify any potential project drivers. Each member of the group independently completed the scoring matrix (see Table 1) by considering each item individually against the others. For an objective considered more important than another a 1 was entered in the box — for less important a zero. Example values are given in Table 1.

Table 1. Scoring matrix to prioritise project objectives

If the objective below is more important than the objective to the right then enter '1' in the box, if not enter '0'.	Time	Cost	Quality	Safety	Environment	Communications	Total
Time		0	0	0	0	1	1
Cost	1		0	0	1	1	3
Quality	1	1		0	1	1	4
Safety	1	1	1		1	1	5
Environment	1	0	0	0		1	2
Communications	0	0	0	0	0		0

The responses from the six group members were summed and gave the following hierarchy:

1.	Safety	30pts
2.	Quality	19pts
3.	Cost	16pts
4.	Environmental	10pts
5.	Time	8pts
6.	Communications	7pts

The results of the ranking exercise were then reviewed and agreed by the workshop to be reasonable at this stage of the risk assessment process.

5. RISK IDENTIFICATION AND PRIORITISATION

Specific construction risks were identified in a brainstorming session, split into three parts:

(*a*) Solo brainstorming
(*b*) Group discussion
(*c*) Checking of risk list

The next step was to use a standard checklist of risks to compare against those already identified and ensure that no relevant risks had been overlooked. In this case the workshop reviewed two lists, namely:

- The checklists in the manual *Construction risk in river and estuary engineering* (Simm and Cruickshank, 1998).
- Environment Agency, *Risk assessment and management manual* (1997a).

Having produced a 'long list' of risks, the following process was applied to produce a list of major risks:

Long list of risks
↓
Short listing
↓
Prioritising
↓
Consolidating

5.1. *Short listing*

The workshop discussed in detail each of the risks identified for the 'long list' in order to remove any risks which were:

- not relevant
- a duplication of another item
- statements rather than risks.

Table 2 details all those identified but in no particular order; the numbered items were selected for inclusion within the 'short list'.

5.2. *Prioritising the risks*

Each of the risks were individually scored against the project objectives, identified earlier in the workshop. The probability of occurrence of each particular risk, and the impact of that risk, should it occur, on each of the selected objectives, were then scored using a scale of 1–5 where 1 was considered 'low' and 5 'high', as shown in Table 3.

When undertaking this assessment it was essential that all participants remained clear as to the risk item considered and how that specific item could affect the specific project objectives.

Usually all the risks would be scored against perhaps two or three outstanding objectives (as decided by the earlier ranking). However, because three objectives did not stand out clearly, a total of four objectives — quality, cost, time and environment — were used. The safety objective was deemed to be dealt with in a separate assessment as this objective is considered by most to be sacrosanct.

6. IDENTIFICATION OF MAJOR RISKS

6.1. *Risks identified by perception*

Prior to risk prioritisation within the workshop, the participants had been asked to generate a list of their top five risks based purely on perception rather than any

Table 2.   List of project risks

	List of risks
1.	Unforeseen ground conditions
2.	Access (condition, restrictions in village, traffic construction)
3.	Noise Quality
4.	Subcontractors' failure to perform
5.	Final breakthrough uncontrollable
6.	Flooding
7.	Embankment stability
8.	General public (access and fishing not available)
9.	Archaeology
10.	Employees — injuries Piling — failure to install Weather — heavy rain
11.	Groundwater — (flooding owing to high groundwater and contamination of groundwater)
12.	Tidal effects and surge
13.	Rare species/habitats discovered Contaminated ground
14.	Pollution of river generally (e.g. oil spillage)
15.	Navigation disruption on canal
16.	Approvals generally
17.	Protesters — delay
18.	Materials supply — lead-in time for prefabrication and other items
19.	Bankrupt contractor Excessive cost
20.	Construction plant (breakdown, unavailability, access) Risk of not constructing to ±3 mm
21.	Off-site accidents in village
22.	Strikes
23.	Site security and trespassers Delivery of concrete
24.	Removal of spoil Frost
25.	Breaching owing to flood
26.	Erosion owing to high flood
27.	Project delayed into new season
28.	Faulty design
29.	Impossible to build — physically

Table 2.   continued

List of risks

30.	Impossible to build — legally
31.	Unforeseen services
32.	War, etc.
33.	OJEC advert delays
34.	Contract variations
35.	Inaccurate data
36.	Inaccurate estimates 3rd party actions
37.	Difficult landowners Water quality in main river Turbidity Vandalism Theft
38.	Fire Faulty modelling
39.	Injunctions
40.	Weather

Table 3.   Calculation of risk score

Risk	Probability of risk occurring: score 1–5	Impact of risk on objective: score 1–5				Total
		Quality	Cost	Environ.	Time	
A	B	C	D	E	F	$B \times (C+D+E+F)$
1. Unforeseen ground conditions	3	1	4	2	4	33
2. Access	3	1	2	3	1	21
3. Noise	2	1	3	4	3	
4. Subcontractor failure	1	3				
5. etc.						

numerical method. This generated the following list:

1.   Flooding
2.   Unforeseen ground conditions
3.   Groundwater
4.   Breaching
5.   Physically impossible to build

6.2. Risks identified by the workshop

The top ten risks identified by the scoring system used within the workshop (detailed in Section 5 above) were as follows:

1. Unforeseen ground conditions
2. Flooding
3. Weather
4. Groundwater (flooding due to high groundwater and contamination of groundwater)
5. Access
6. Embankment stability
7. Removal of spoil
8. Contract variations
9. Inaccurate data
10. Inaccurate estimates

6.3. Real project risks

Since the workshop example was based around a real construction project, the risks identified, and those that actually occurred during the project, could also be listed for comparison with both the workshop derived risks and the perceived risks. During the real project the following risk items were identified (in no particular order):

- flooding/breaching of cut
- unforeseen ground conditions/embankment stability
- groundwater
- access
- noise/environment
- difficulty to build — construction tolerances.

6.4. Conclusions

When comparing the perceived risks against those identified through the workshop process, the workshop participants generally agreed that the workshop results were perhaps more realistic and the following was noted:

- It is often difficult for the mind to separate out risk probability and risk consequence. It was felt that the risk workshop helped in this process.
- The results of the workshop assessment reflected the objectives used. If different objectives had been used then a different risk list or order of priority may well have been generated.

6.5. Actual project risks, mitigation measures and incidents

In the event, the following measures were taken to mitigate the construction risks identified, and the following incidents occurred (or not!):

Flooding/breaching of cut

Mitigation measures:	Water levels in the river around the site were lowered and kept low throughout the construction period. Advance warning of any flood events was given via a flood warning system.
Occurrences:	No problems.

Unforeseen ground conditions/embankment stability

Mitigation measures:	Early site investigation. Design and construction method to avoid excavation close to existing banks.
Occurrences:	Minor erosion problems at toe of embankment due to rainfall runoff.

Groundwater

Mitigation measures:	Use of a network of pumps to lower groundwater. Advance testing of system to ensure suitability.
Occurrences:	No problems.

Access

Mitigation measures:	Second access point secured for part of project. Good relations established and maintained with community (public displays, etc.).
Occurrences:	No problems.

Noise/environment

Mitigation measures:	Excavated material used to create and landscape bunds between the site and local housing. This reduced both noise and visual intrusion.
Occurrences:	Minimal.

Building issues — construction tolerances

Mitigation measures:	High quality steel shuttering and geotextiles were used to cast the siphon hoods. A test cast was made first to establish tolerances.
Occurrences:	No problems.

Weather — difficulty with earthworks

Mitigation measures: Plan construction through summer.
Occurrences: Continued bad weather delayed the project through water-logging of the site. Plant mobility was reduced and excavation difficult/impossible.
                       Run-off from embankments caused local erosion of landscaped material.

7.   GENERATION OF THE RISK PORTFOLIO

An example 'risk portfolio' was generated within the workshop. The risk portfolio is designed to be a tool for the Project Manager to monitor, control and manage risks throughout a project. A risk portfolio would contain the following items.

Detailed description of the risk
As developed through the workshop discussions.

Risk management action plan
Describing each of the elements involved in responding to the risk. This can involve a number of actions under the following headings:

- remove risk
- reduce risk
- share risk
- transfer risk
- insure risk
- accept risk

The action plan should attempt to control the risk by first removing the risk. If this is not possible then the plan should attempt to reduce, then share, then transfer and so on.

Responsibility chain
The individual and/or organisation responsible for dealing with each element of the risk management action plan.

Timescale
The period during the project when the risk is relevant, along with any deadlines and crucial dates pertinent to the risk.

Residual risks
Risks arising as a result of the chosen risk management action plan(s).

Figure 1.   Risk portfolio for particular risk item

Risk portfolio

Risk

Siphons — Impossible to physically build

Description

Construction of the siphon requires high quality and tight tolerances. Therefore the forming of the reinforced concrete siphons will be difficult to build. The risk is that the quality and tolerances required will not be possible to achieve.

Risk management action plan

Remove
- Investigate change to another design which requires more relaxed quality and tolerances
- Apply construction techniques used in similar projects where tight tolerances and high quality were required

Reduce
- Precasting
- Permanent shuttering
- Use experienced reinforced concrete contractor
- Modify the design where possible
- Build test section on land

Share
- Advance precasting
- Nominated precasting contractor

Transfer
- None identified/applicable

Accept
- Not an option

Insure
- Not applicable

Responsibility chain
- Project manager

Timescale
- During design and procurement

Residual risks (risks arising as a result of the action plan)
- Cost implications of action plan — but will produce a better fixed cost estimate

---

Cost implications
- To be identified ahead of putting the action plan into practice

---

Control
- Check progress of action plan monthly during design and procurement phase

---

Cost allowance

The budget allocated for dealing with the risk, and who pays. This section will be completed when a budget is allocated for the project and may involve post-workshop discussions.

Means of control

The control procedure in place that ensures that the risk management action plans will be followed.

Owing to time constraints, members of the workshop were only able to develop the risk portfolio for one of the identified risks. The risk chosen was:

Siphons — physically impossible to build?

Figure 1 shows the risk portfolio developed for this particular risk item.

8.   POST WORKSHOP ACTIVITIES

A number of follow up actions would usually be agreed upon by the workshop. These would typically include the following.

- Enhancing the cost plan. The independent facilitator would meet with the Project Manager and Cost Engineer to gain information for developing the cost plan and to cost the major risks.
- Creation of a risk calendar based on the information generated by the risk management workshop.
- Calculation of contingencies required for the project.
- Production of a risk register detailing all of the risks identified during the workshop. Such a register would be used by the Project Manager to control risks throughout the project.

Annex 1.
Project details

1. ## INTRODUCTION

    It is proposed to construct a new river channel and control structure at Low Fradling. The Client wishes to replace an ageing weir on a river that is directly linked to a navigable canal. The structure will be a large air-regulated siphon weir and will control flows and levels in both the river and the canal.

    A preliminary design for the project has been prepared by Traditional Consultants Ltd. Just prior to commissioning the tender design, the Client suddenly thought that it would be a good idea to hold a risk workshop and asked Risk Consultants Ltd to undertake this process. The Client has briefed Risk Consultants Ltd that they have fully examined the project risks internally and wish them only to examine construction risks for the project.

    The Client has pre-qualified six contractors for the project. Risk Consultants Ltd invited these contractors to attend the risk workshop. Of the six invited, three declined saying they were too busy, one had gone bankrupt, and one stated that he knew all of the risks and did not wish to share them with his competitors or the Client. Only Traditional Contractors Ltd wanted to attend.

    Risk Consultants Ltd asked the Client to formulate their construction objectives for the project. Initially the Client outlined these as detailed below:

    - Time — project to be completed by April 2000
    - Cost — price certainty is paramount
    - Quality — high precision required for weir construction to ensure smooth operation; aesthetics important
    - Safety — operation of the canal and flows in the river must not be affected during the contract, consideration must be given to the stability of local embankments
    - Communication — as specified below
    - Environment — effects on the environment must be kept to a minimum during construction: noisy works outside hours 7 a.m. to 7 p.m. are prohibited and disruption to the public must be kept to a minimum
    - Others — none identified to date

    However, Risk Consultants Ltd stated that the above objectives were not necessarily:

Simple
Measurable
Achievable
Realistic
Time bound

The Client has promised to review them at the workshop.

2. THE SITE

There is only one access route to the site and this goes through the village of Low Fradling. The Client has stated that there should be minimal disruption to the village. The construction area is adjacent to an SSSI which attracts a lot of birdwatchers and fishermen. A public right of way crosses the area. The Client has stated that it is the contractors responsibility to ensure that any disturbance to the amenity users is kept to a minimum.

3. RIVER FLOWS AND WATER LEVELS

River flow and water level at the site is influenced by a combination of sluice operation on the canal, local weir operation (Old Weir) and operation of another weir downstream. Tidal influence can be felt at the site under high spring or surge tide conditions.

Upon request, the Environment Agency have provided the following information:

- Flows up to 140 m³/s pass down the river.
- Flows in excess of 140 m³/s are passed along the canal, maintaining 140 m³/s in the river.
- It is estimated that a mean daily flow into the canal of 220 m³/s has a return period of 0·25, while a flow of 650 m³/s has a return period of 20 years.
- A 100-year flood event comprises a flow of 800 m³/s which gives a flow of 220 m³/s in the river.

Spring tides and tidal surges can affect water levels at the site. This occurs approximately 120 times per year. An estimate of normal and surge levels at the site is given in Table 4.

4. ENGINEERING ASPECTS

The project involves:

- excavation of a new river channel
- construction of a new control structure.

Table 4.   Tide and surge water levels at Low Fradling

Return period flood:	Total flow:	River flow:	Water level at site: (m ODN)		Water level with HAT: m ODN	Water level 100-year surge: m ODN
1 in year	m³/s	m³/s	d/s	u/s	d/s	d/s
0·25	220	140	7·0	8·4	7·4	7·8
20	650	140	7·0	8·4	7·4	7·8
100	800	220	8·0	8·7	8·1	8·4

Note: d/s = downstream; u/s = upstream

An overview of the site and the proposed new works location is shown in Figure 2.

4.1. Excavation of a new river channel

When considering design and construction of the new river channel the following points should be noted:

- The proposed river channel cuts across an existing river meander and bypasses the old weir.
- The land is adjacent to large embanked areas used to store dredged material from the Canal.
- The channel route crosses an old, infilled river meander.
- An old disused canal channel runs along the north edge of the land.
- The new channel cuts across an existing public right of way.
- The channel has been designed to include environmental features such as bends and berms.
- Landscaping and a small island are proposed to enhance environmental features.

4.2. Construction of the new control structure

The new structure comprises nine air-regulated siphon bays, with two overflow weirs, a fish pass and a large stilling basin downstream. Bed and bank protection is required around the structure itself.

Air entrainment through the siphons is an essential part of their operation. This means that construction tolerances for the weir crests and hood must be within ±3 mm. A high-quality finish is required to the weir surfaces.

Excavation must not endanger the stability of the adjacent embankments.

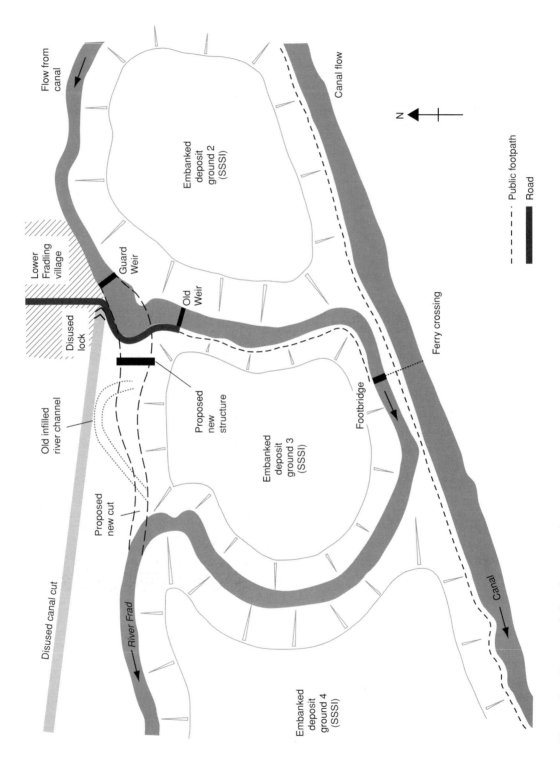

Figure 2. Proposed development site

5.   CONTRACT TIMING

The tender design is to be completed by March 1999, put out to tender from April to May 1999 and final funding approvals to be in place by September 1999.

The contract is to be let in October 1999 and to be completed by April 2000 to fit with local wildlife constraints.

Annex 2.
Blank forms for use in a workshop

Prioritising objectives

If the objective below is more important than the objective to the right then enter '1' in the box, if not enter '0'.	Time	Cost	Quality	Safety	Environment	Communications	Total
Time							
Cost							
Quality							
Safety							
Environment							
Communications							

Prioritising the risks

	A	B	C	D	E	F	G
Item no.	Risk	Probability of risk occurring 1–5	Impact on objective 1–5				Total B × (C+D+E+F)

Note: 1 = low probability/impact; 5 = high probability/impact

Risk portfolio

Risk portfolio

Risk

Description

Risk management action plan

Remove
-
-

Reduce
-
-

Share
-
-

Transfer
-
-

Accept
-
-

Insure
-
-

Responsibility chain
-
-

Timescale
-
-

Residual risks (risks arising as a result of the action plan)
-
-

Cost implications
-
-

Control
-
-

Appendix 4.
Perrancoombe Stream flood-area study.
Test-case application of CIRIA SP125
methodology

A4.1. SUMMARY

This case study details the first application of CIRIA SP125 risk assessment techniques to an Environment Agency (EA) construction project. The technique has been applied from a client's perspective and includes identification of key risk issues, estimation of probability of occurrence, their subsequent costs and the application of Monte Carlo style analysis to produce a probability – cost curve. This approach to risk management was shared with all parties throughout the project. Probability and cost estimates were undertaken at three points during the study prior to tender, at 50% completion and following completion. A comparison of available data for the varying probability (cost curves) is given along with conclusions and recommendations on application of the procedure to such a construction project.

The case study is presented under the following sections:

- Project background
- Flood problem
- Proposed scheme
- Risk issues
- Risk assessment approach
- Initial risk assessment
- Mid-term risk assessment
- End of project risk assessment
- Conclusions and recommendations

A4.2. PROJECT BACKGROUND

The town of Perranporth lies at the downstream end of the Perrancoombe Stream catchment, at the outlet of the stream into the sea at Perran Beach (Figure A4.1). The town of Perranporth has a thriving summer tourist industry centred around this beach. The stream passes through the town and there are no flood protection measures. Prior to reaching the town the stream passes through a predominantly rural, steep-sided valley.

A4.3. FLOOD PROBLEM

Serious flooding of property has occurred in the town of Perranporth in recent years. Notable flooding occurred during October 1988, December 1993 and

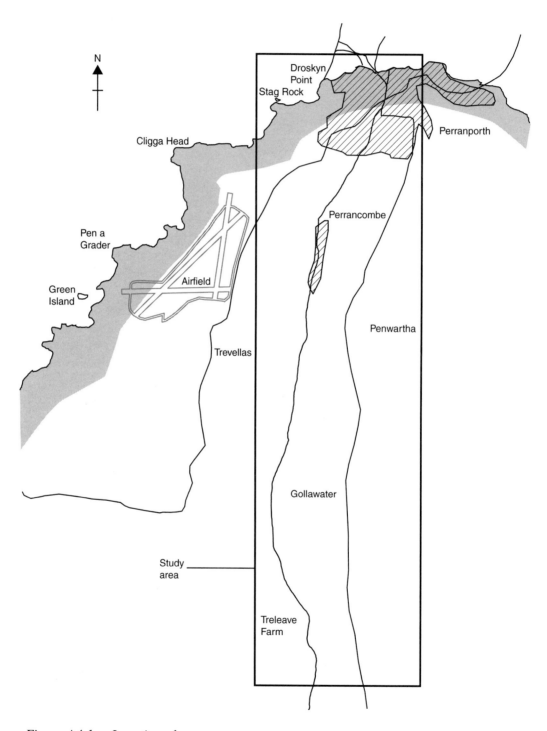

Figure A4.1. Location plan

January 1994. Flooding occurs rapidly once flow in the stream exceeds bank-full levels as the channel is perched in the area where it passes through the town (Figure A4.2). In addition to the fluvial flooding there is local surface flooding of some low-lying areas of the town.

Comparing the estimated stream capacity, at bank-full conditions, against predicted storm-event flows may identify the cause of the flooding problem. The in-bank flow capacity of the Perrancoombe Stream was calculated to be 3·5 m³/s. This discharge was estimated to have a 1 in 2·33 year return period (i.e. the mean annual flood). By undertaking an FSR analysis using catchment characteristics, storm-event discharges were calculated for the stream. Peak discharges were estimated as:

1 in 50 year return-period event	Flow = 9·2 m³/s
1 in 75 year return-period event	Flow = 10·0 m³/s
1 in 100 year return-period event	Flow = 10·6 m³/s
1 in 200 year return period event	Flow = 12·2 m³/s

Since the bank-full capacity of the stream roughly equalled the peak discharge of the MAF and the stream was perched in areas through the town, then for any event greater that a MAF there would inevitably be some flooding. For example, for a return-period event of 1 in 50 year, there would be an excess flow of 5·7 m³/s.

A4.4. PROPOSED SCHEME

An assessment was made of possible flood-alleviation options, their environmental impact and the benefit cost-ratio obtained. The preferred option chosen by the EA provided the least environmental impact and had the highest benefit cost-ratio. The proposed layout for this scheme, at the feasibility stage, is shown in

Figure A4.2.   Raised river wall along Tywarnhayle Square

Figure A4.3. The level of flood protection offered by the preferred scheme was for the 1 in 75 year return-period flood event.

The chosen solution dealt with excess flood discharge during storm conditions by diverting the flow along a combination of 1·65 m diameter circular pipelines and a concrete box culvert, with an approximate length of 665 m. Figure A4.4 is a concept sketch of the culvert and channel tie-in to the beach outlet channel. In addition, these works would be supplemented by the widening and re-profiling of the existing stream, both upstream and downstream of the new culvert, to ensure sufficient open-channel capacity. The modified channel would have a split-level or two-stage channel, so as to accommodate both low and peak discharge. The total length of widening and re-profiling of the stream is approximately 215 m as shown in Figures A4.5 and A4.6.

In addition to the main flood-alleviation works, minor improvements to river walls, bridges and the town centre drainage system, were also proposed.

Construction of the scheme was scheduled to take place between September 1997 and June 1998.

A4.5. RISK ISSUES

Throughout the environmental study, site investigation, concept design and detail design, risk issues were identified and noted. Prior to tendering the preferred scheme, an engineer's report was prepared by the Environment Agency. This contained the design-stage risk register that summarised risks and the proposed ownership of those risks (between client and contractor). Six key risk issues were identified prior to the start of construction work with sub-divisions within several of these risks. A short discussion of the risk issues identified in the risk register is given below. Table A4.1 provides full details from the design-stage risk register.

Archaeological features
The desk study did not reveal any features other than mine workings along the route of the proposed culvert. However, as part of the construction works, there was an archaeological watching-brief to ensure that any discovery was recorded at an early date. Plans were made such that any discovery could be dealt with as efficiently as possible to reduce any potential delays to the project.

Environmental

Ground contamination. The original site-investigation works identified ground contamination as a risk, hence further investigations had been undertaken to identify the level of contamination that could be expected. Although this had been undertaken, there still remained a residual risk that the contamination levels in some areas could be higher than expected.

Pollution by contaminated material. During excavation of contaminated ground material there was a potential risk that the material could pollute the stream and

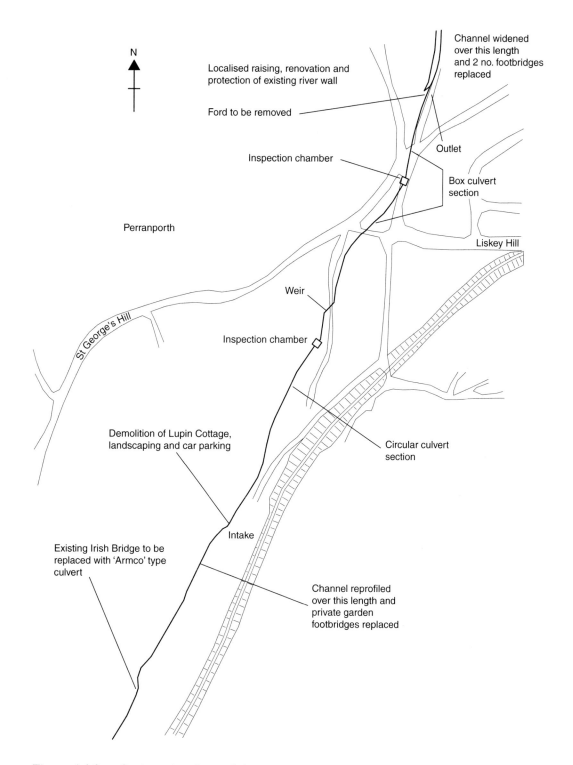

Figure A4.3.   Options A$_{50}$, A$_{75}$ and A$_{100}$

hence the beach. The primary measure taken to reduce and minimise the risk was to agree contingency plans with the EA Water Quality Officer. Typical examples were that water from the excavated trench would be 'settled' in the boating lake and that water quality would be monitored in the stream.

Pollution by general construction work.   As with all construction works in a river or stream there is the risk of pollution from works activity. This risk was

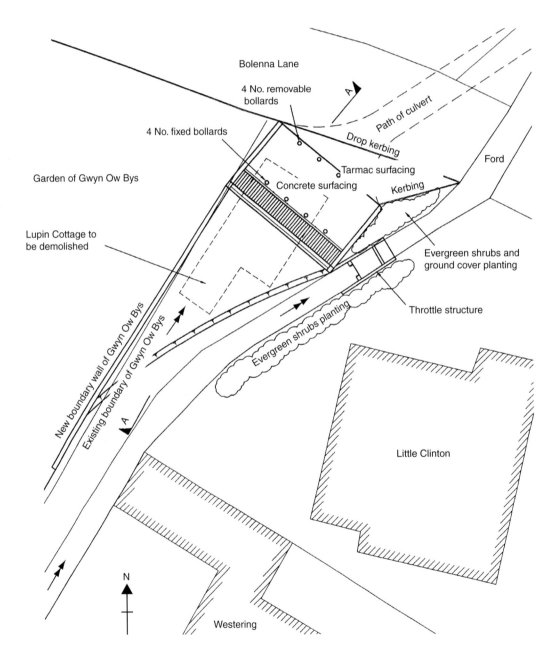

Figure A4.4.   Location plan of inlet works

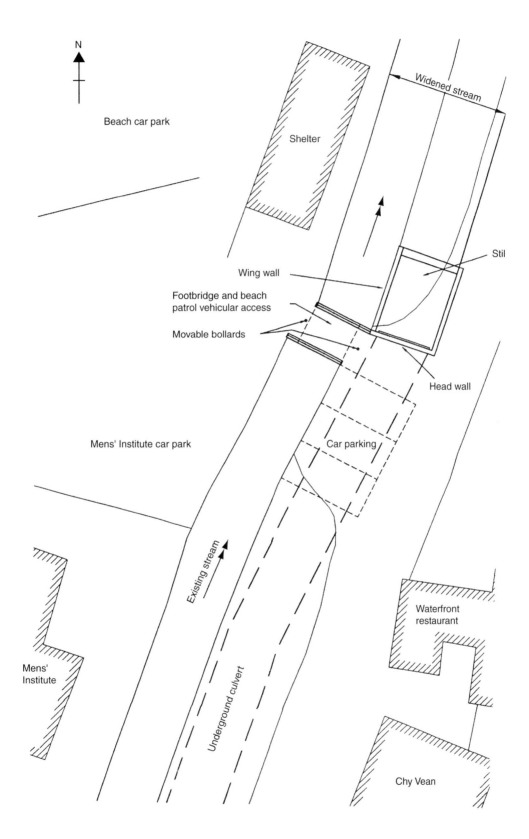

Figure A4.5.   Plan of outlet to beach

Table A4.1. Design-stage risk register

Risk no.	Residual risk	Proba-bility	Severity of financial consequence	Mitigation action already undertaken	Further mitigation action
R1	Archaeological				
R1.1	Archaeological feature discovered on culvert route	15%	M	Desk study has not revealed evidence of features apart from mine workings	Specify archaeological watching brief to identify
R2	Environmental				
R2.1	Ground contamination levels substantially higher than predicted	4%	L	Main and secondary ground investigations carried out to establish contamination levels	
R2.2	Pollution of stream, and hence beach from contaminated ground	4%	M	Approach agreed with EA Water Quality Officer	Specify dewatering water to be discharged to the completed culvert as constructed. Water from trench to be settled in boating lake. Monitor water quality
R2.3	Pollution of stream from general construction work		0		Specify contractor to avoid use of stream for access where possible. Standard EA clauses 1.14.1 to 7. Monitor water quality
R2.4	Pollution of beach from general construction work		0		Specification to restrict working area on the beach and control beach operations
R2.5	Landfill tax: some material on site is discovered which is 'active' waste and therefore attracts higher rate of tax	5%	VL	Discussions with waste regulator indicated low rate of tax applicable based on ground investigation results	

Table A4.1. continued

R3	Dewatering				
R3.1	Dewatering fails to operate effectively		0	Ground investigation reports give contractor details of ground conditions and therefore appropriate dewatering techniques	
R3.2	Dewatering causes property settlement and damage to services	25%	H	Approximate zone of influence for dewatering determined to assess number of properties that could be affected	Specification for dewatering to minimise risk of settlement. Specify pre-construction property survey
R3.3	Higher rates of dewatering required because soil is of higher permeability than predicted	3%	M	Ground investigation results give contractor details of soil permeability	
R4	Mine workings				
R4.1	Mine workings discovered during construction	12%	L	Culvert routed away from known mineshafts	Specify contractor to have procedures to note and act on warning signs. Restrict 'vibration causing' operations and those significantly affecting groundwater regime. Contractor to include in tender a cost for a two week delay to allow for a mine capping operation
R4.2	Mineshaft collapses (due to increased water flow from dewatering, excavation or construction vibration)	5%	H	As above	Specify contractor to have procedures to note and act on the warning signs. Restrict 'vibration causing' operations and those significantly affecting groundwater regime

Table A4.1.   continued

Risk no.	Residual risk	Proba-bility	Severity of financial consequence	Mitigation action already undertaken	Further mitigation action
R4.3	Multiple mineshaft collapse	1·4%	VH	As above	As above
R5	Damage to property				
R5.1	Damage to adjacent properties where excavating in close proximity	15%	M	Works designed to minimise works near properties	Specify pre-construction property survey. Contractor's method statement to ensure he minimises risk
R6	Flooding				
R6.1	Severe flooding, beyond what a contractor might reasonably expect	3%	M	Analysis of flood frequency carried out	

Note:
- Table to be read in conjunction with risk cost-estimation table (Table A4.2).
- Probability and financial consequence are given for the medium-risk case (see Table A4.2 for definition). Financial consequences which are the contractor's risk are zero rated.
- Financial consequences are divided into the following bands: VL: 0–£5000, L: £5000–£10 000, M: £10 000–£100 000, H: £100 000–£500 000, VH: >£500 000.
- 'Usual' construction risks, i.e. risks inherent in any large flood-defence project such as delays due to a site accident, have not been included.
- All mitigation actions are the responsibility of the consultant to specify in contract documents and the contractor to carry out on-site unless otherwise stated above.
- There are no significant secondary risks caused by the mitigation actions identified above.

minimised through the use of specific conditions within the contract that, whenever possible, restricted the contractor from using the stream for access.

Landfill tax.   While the site investigations gave a good indication of the levels of contaminated materials that could be expected from excavation at the site, there is an element of risk left due to potential variation in the level of contamination. As such, disposal costs could also potentially vary.

Dewatering
Dewatering system not efficient.   Under normal conditions of contract for construction works, the risk of not having an efficient dewatering system rests with the contractor, however, this risk may be minimised by providing the contractor with all the factual site investigation material available.

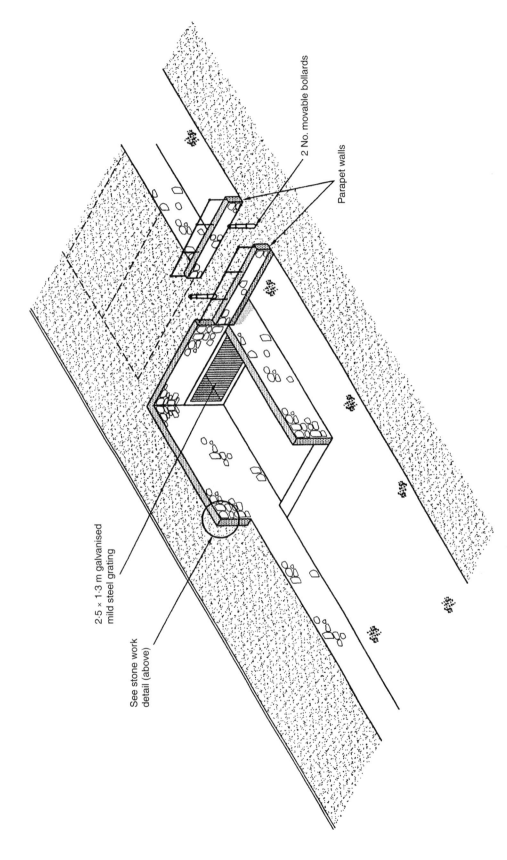

2 No. movable bollards

Parapet walls

2·5 × 1·3 m galvanised
mild steel grating

See stone work
detail (above)

Figure A4.6.   Isometric view of outlet to beach

Dewatering causes property settlement. During dewatering of the works, there will be a risk of settlement to adjacent properties. As part of the preliminary studies an assessment of the likely zone of influence due to dewatering was established which allowed the number of properties that may be affected to be determined. Mitigation measures could therefore be established, in the event of settlement occurring. In addition, the need was identified to undertake base-line surveys of properties, prior to commencement of dewatering, in order to minimise the potential for dispute later in the project.

Additional dewatering. Even with extensive site investigation, there is always a residual risk that additional dewatering will be required if the soil permeability is greater than expected. There are no mitigation measures that can be applied in this instance although contingency plans may be identified.

Mine workings

Discovery of workings during construction. In areas such as Perranporth where extensive mining has taken place there is always a risk of exposing unrecorded mine workings. The main mitigation measure that can be adopted is to ensure that the route of the proposed culvert avoids any known mine shafts. Also, the contractor's work procedures required that he watch for and monitor any warning signs of mine workings and develop contingency plans for action in case of discovery.

Single or multiple mineshaft collapse(s). During the construction period there would be a risk of mineshaft collapse due to increased groundwater flow, excavation or vibration around a shaft. Again, the main mitigation measure that could be undertaken is to avoid known shaft areas in the alignment of the culvert route. Watching for warning signs was an important aspect within the contractors working procedures and construction techniques that involve vibration were to be minimised wherever possible.

Damage to properties

Excavation adjacent to existing properties can cause both nuisance and possible collapse or failure of the structure. A basic mitigation measure is to avoid a route that entails close proximity working. As with many residual risks, provided the contractor is aware of them, then the work method can be tailored to suit the potential problem. Existing property surveys are important in these instances, to record the condition of the property prior to starting construction.

Severe flooding

Within the construction conditions of contract, there is normally provision for reimbursement for inclement weather conditions. Clearly, flash flooding or unusual events can be an additional risk. This can be minimised by undertaking a flood-frequency analysis, prior to the construction being awarded.

A4.6. RISK ASSESSMENT APPROACH

The risk assessment methodology applied was based on the EA *Control of risk manual*. The objective of the risk assessment is defined as 'the completion of the project within budget'. Techniques proposed by the EA follow recommendations made within the CIRIA SP125 (CIRIA, 1996a) report.

A risk register for the project was prepared which identified key risks and possible mitigation measures. The risk issues identified in Section A4.5 above were all taken from this risk register. Table A4.1 contains details of these risks.

A cost contingency analysis was then undertaken for the project. This method provides a systematic approach for allocating cost allowances to all risk items. The approach initially has two components:

(*a*) To allocate a contingency of 10% to work items for which there is high confidence (i.e. non-risk items).
(*b*) To create a set of probability/cost scenarios for each of the risk items identified in the risk register. By applying a sampling technique to these items a probability distribution of risk cost may be calculated.

By combining cost estimates from steps (*a*) and (*b*), an estimate of the total risk cost-probability distribution may be found.

A4.7. INITIAL RISK ASSESSMENT

While Table A4.1 provides details of the key risks identified and presented in the risk register, Table A4.2 presents the probability of occurrence and subsequent cost-estimates associated with each of these risks. Note that each item has been divided into four event-categories, which are the no, low, medium and high impacts. The selection of these values has been based on engineering experience and judgement. Where the risk owner has been identified as the contractor, the item has been removed from the assessment since the analysis has been undertaken for budget control on behalf of the Environment Agency.

For this particular study a computer simulation based on the Monte Carlo sampling technique was applied with 40 000 iterations to obtain the probability distribution. Table A4.3 presents the results from just one of the 40 000 iterations showing the random selection of risk costs. Table A4.4 presents a summary printout upon completion of the analysis, showing maximum values that have been selected during the process and hence confirming that the analysis has run for a sufficient period of time to provide an accurate estimation of cost distribution.

Figure A4.7 shows the probability of cost over-run. Two confidence limits of 50% and 95% give estimated costs for the risk elements of £178 000 and £529 000 respectively.

Table A4.2.   Risk cost-estimation

Risk no.	Case	Probability	Description	Cost basis	Cost: £000s
R1.1	No event	76%			0
	Low	15%	Minor remains of little archaeological value or easily movable.	1 day delay plus £1000 additional archaeological staff costs	8
	Medium	6%	More significant remains necessitating more extensive recording	6 day delay plus £10 000 archaeological investigation costs	52
	High	3%	Extensive remains of high archaeological value	4 month delay resulting in the need for contractor to demobilise/remobilise. £25000 archaeological investigation costs	75
R2.1	No event	86%			0
	Low	8%	100 m^3 of spoil with > 1000 ppm arsenic requiring more stringent protective measures and disposal	Quote of additional £41 per m^3 above non-contaminated disposal costs (KS/PERR/26 18/1/96). Therefore £41 − £15·6 = £25·4 per m^3 more than used in appraisal report	2·5
	Medium	4%	300 m^3 with > 1000 ppm arsenic	Cost basis as above	7·5
	High	2%	1500 m^3 with > 1000 ppm arsenic	Cost basis as above	38
R2.2	No event	86%			0
	Low	8%	200 m^3 of beach sand has to be removed and placed	Allow £30 per m^3 for removal, disposal and importing correctly-graded sand and placement	6
	Medium	4%	600 m^3 of beach sand has to be removed and placed	As above	18
	High	2%	1900 m^3 of beach sand has to be removed and placed	As above	57

Table A4.2.   continued

R2.3	Contractor's risk				
R2.4	Contractor's risk				
R2.5	No event	85%			0
	Low	8%	50 m^3 of spoil has to be reclassified as 'active waste'	Landfill tax of £14 per m^3 (increase of £10 per m^3)	0·5
	Medium	5%	200 m^3 of spoil has to be reclassified as 'active waste'	As above	2
	High	2%	1000 m^3 of spoil has to be reclassified as 'active waste'	As above	10
R3.1	Contractor's risk				
R3.2	No event	2%			0
	Low	40%	6 properties with minor cracking (requiring internal redecoration) and no service disruption	Allow £10 000 per property for internal redecoration and compensation	60
	Intermediate	30%	10 properties with minor cracking, 1 property with major cracking (requiring internal decoration and external re-rendering) and minor repairs	£10 000 per property for minor cracking. £40 000 for major cracking and £5000 for service repairs	145
	Medium	25%	12 properties with minor cracking and 2 properties with major cracking. Minor service repairs	A. N. Other's estimate of cost of works including compensation (memo of 28/5/96) and £10 000 allowance for servicing repairs	230
	High	3%	As above and also 1 property suffers severe cracking and has to be rebuilt. More major service repairs	Extrapolation of the above allowing £180 000 for rebuilding and including £50 000 allowance for service repairs	450

Table A4.2. continued

Risk no.	Case	Probability	Description	Cost basis	Cost: £000s
R3.3	No event	85%			0
	Low	10%	Soil permeability is an order of magnitude higher than anticipated over 10% of the route	Increase estimate of dewatering costs by 10%, i.e.10% of £160 000. Includes allowance for delay	16
	Medium	3%	Soil permeability is an order of magnitude higher than anticipated over 30% of the route	Increase estimate of dewatering costs by 30%, i.e. 30% of £160 000. Includes allowance for delay	48
	High	2%	Soil permeability is an order of magnitude higher than anticipated over 60% of the route	Increase estimate of dewatering costs by 60%, i.e. 60% of £160 000. Includes allowance for delay	96
R4.1	No event	76%			0
	Low	6%	Shaft upstream-end of works where there are high rock-levels	Capping works, no services damaged, no property damage and no delay	2·5
	Medium	12%	Shaft in area of playing fields or Boscawen Gardens, away from property	Capping works, minor service damage, no property damage and half a day delay	8
	High	6%	Shaft in downstream section adjacent to properties or adjacent to Boscawen Gardens properties	Capping works, £10 000 for services repair, £50 000 for property repairs/ compensation and 2 day delay	82
R4.2	No event	92%			0
	Low	1%	Shaft fails in upstream end of works away from properties	As R4.1 medium case	8
	Medium	5%	Shaft fails nearer properties	As R3.2 medium case plus 2 day delay	244

Table A4.2.   continued

	High	2%	Shaft fails near properties. 1 property requires rebuilding	As R3.2 high case plus demobilisation/ remobilization costs	500
R4.3	No event	97·6%			0
	Low	0·5%	2 shafts fail in the upstream end of the works away from properties	2 times R4.2 low case	16
	Medium	1·4%	2 shafts fail. 3 properties have to be rebuilt	3 times R3.2 high case plus demobilisation/ remobilization costs	1400
	High	0·5%	3 shafts fail in a densely built-up area. 6 properties have to be rebuilt	6 times R3.2 2 high case plus demobilisation/ remobilization costs	2750
R5.1	No event	50%			0
	Low	30%	2 properties with minor cracking	A third of R3.2 low case	20
	Medium	15%	1 major cracking, additional underpinning works and 1 day delay	£40 000 for major cracking plus delay costs	47
	High	5%	1 property fails, rebuild and 2 day delay	£180 000 for rebuilding plus delay costs	194
R6.1	No event	88·75%	Flood event < 1 in 5 year		0
	Low	7·5%	1 in 10-year event	Loss of material and 1 day delay	12
	Medium	3%	1 in 25-year event	Loss of material, minor damage to plant and 2 day delay	30
	High	0·75%	1 in 50-year event	Loss of material, damage to plant and delay	80

Note:
- Table to be read in conjunction with the design-stage risk register (Table A4.1)
- Scenario definition:

No event	self explanatory
Low	low-cost scenario (given that a significant event has occurred)
Intermediate	cost between low and medium scenarios
Medium	medium-cost scenario
High	highest-cost scenario

Table A4.3.   Results for one run from the Monte Carlo simulation

Perrancoombe Stream flood alleviation scheme
Cost contingency analysis

Code	Risk	Estimate	Cost: £	Probability	Distribution: Fn
R1.1	Archaeology	N	0	0·76	
		L	8000	0·15	
		M	52 000	0·06	
		H	75 000	0·03	8000
R2.1	Contamination disposal	N	0	0·86	
		L	2500	0·08	
		M	7500	0·04	
		H	10 000	0·02	0
R2.2	Beach pollution	N	0	0·86	
		L	6000	0·08	
		M	18 000	0·04	
		H	57 000	0·02	0
R2.5	Landfill Tax	N	0	0·85	
		L	500	0·08	
		M	2000	0·05	
		H	10 000	0·02	500
R3.2	Dewatering settlement	N	0	0·02	
		L	60 000	0·4	
		I	145 000	0·3	
		M	230 000	0·25	
		H	450 000	0·03	145 000
R3.3	Dewatering underestimate	N	0	0·85	
		L	16 000	0·1	
		M	48 000	0·03	
		H	96 000	0·02	0
R4.1	Mine capping	N	0	0·76	
		L	2500	0·06	
		M	8000	0·12	
		H	82 000	0·06	8000
R4.2	Mine shaft collapse	N	0	0·92	
		L	8000	0·01	
		M	244 000	0·05	
		H	500 000	0·02	8000
R4.3	Multiple shaft collapse	N	0	0·976	
		L	16 000	0·005	
		M	1 400 000	0·014	
		H	2 750 000	0·005	16 000

Table A4.3.   continued

R5.1	Damage to nearby properties	N	0	0·5	
		L	20 000	0·3	
		M	47 000	0·15	
		H	194 000	0·05	20 000
R6.1	Flooding	N	0	0·8875	
		L	12 000	0·075	
		M	30 000	0·03	
		H	80 000	0·0075	0
				Sum total	205 500

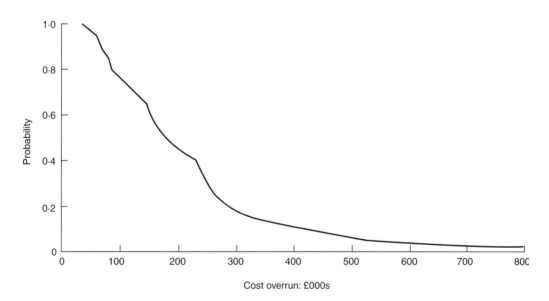

Figure A4.7.   Plot of probability-cost overrun

A4.8. MID-TERM RISK ASSESSMENT

At the mid point during the project a review of the risk assessment figures was undertaken and a revised estimate of remaining financial risk made. In reviewing and updating the assessment almost all of the risk outcomes remain unchanged, however the probability of occurrence of most of the risks was significantly reduced.

Table A4.4. Summary statistics

Simulation results for PERRMAV1.XLS

Iterations = 40 000
Simulations = 1
# Input variables = 11
# Output variables = 1
Sampling type = Monte Carlo
Run time = 00:18:11

Summary statistics

Cell	Name	Minimum	Mean	Maximum
F53	(Sim#1) Sum total H/DISTRIBUTION F . . .	0	241 788	3 710 000
F10	(Sim#1) (Input) H/DISTRIBUTION . . .	0	6549·9	75 000
F14	(Sim#1) (Input) H/DISTRIBUTION . . .	0	700	10 000
F18	(Sim#1) (Input) H/DISTRIBUTION . . .	0	2400·375	57 000
F22	(Sim#1) (Input) H/DISTRIBUTION . . .	0	335·3125	10 000
F27	(Sim#1) (Input) H/DISTRIBUTION . . .	0	138 638·3	450 000
F31	(Sim#1) (Input) H/DISTRIBUTION . . .	0	5069·2	96 000
F35	(Sim#1) (Input) H/DISTRIBUTION . . .	0	6188·413	82 000
F39	(Sim#1) (Input) H/DISTRIBUTION . . .	0	21 986·7	500 000
F43	(Sim#1) (Input) H/DISTRIBUTION . . .	0	34 796·5	2 750 000
F47	(Sim#1) (Input) H/DISTRIBUTION . . .	0	22 700·68	194 000
F51	(Sim#1) (Input) H/DISTRIBUTION . . .	0	2422·65	80 000

The risk assessment undertaken at the design stage proved a valuable tool as during the first half of the contract there were several increases in cost including:

- a mineshaft encountered on the culvert line
- disposal of heavily-contaminated ground leading to higher than expected cost
- delays due to known services being greater than expected
- unidentified services encountered
- cost of archaeology greater than expected, although no finds on site to date
- site supervision costs greater than estimated
- obstructions to piling (unforeseen ground conditions).

Some of the above were included in the design-stage risk assessment and some were not. Since the costs of these events were now largely known they could now be included in the 'certain' costs and do not feature in the ongoing risk assessment except where recurrence was possible.

It is clear that by having made an assessment of the possible costs associated with risks identified before the start of the project, this provided a framework within which the occurrence of additional costs were treated more reasonably rather than coming as an unwelcome shock. This encouraged a better working atmosphere between client and contractor for the project. In addition, having already identified possible mitigation measures required for each of the anticipated risks, the project team was well prepared to respond to any of these incidents when they occurred.

Two additional risks were identified and included in the mid-term analysis as follows:

- The risk of increased compensation claims principally due to the prolonging of works in Tywarnhale Square. This was based on estimated costs from the contractor and has been assumed to be a triangular distribution with a mean of £25 000, and upper and lower bounds of £55 000 and £5000 respectively.
- The risk of variation in the contract final-account due to re-measurement. The Resident Engineer monitored measurement to date on the contract and the revised estimate was based on this. However, there remains a risk of variation and this has been assumed to take the form of a triangular distribution about a mean of zero and with upper and lower bounds of £18 000 and −£5000 respectively.

As with the initial risk-assessment, revised tabular and cost data was calculated, namely:

Table A4.5   50% construction-stage risk register
Table A4.6   50% construction risk-cost estimation table
Table A4.7   Estimated out-turn costs
Figure A4.8   Probability cost distribution at the 50% completion stage

By studying these results it can be seen that without the risk elements, the current projected total out-turn estimate is £2 077 499 against the currently approved sum of £2 086 633.

The 50-percentile risk has reduced to £52 466 from £178 000 at the design stage. This now gives a total final estimate, with 50% risk items, of £2 129 965 compared with the currently approved estimate of £2 264 633. The 95-percentile risk has reduced to £262 000 from £529 000.

From the graph of probability against cost over-run, it can be seen that there is currently a 91% probability of the works out-turn cost being within the currently approved (with 50% risk) estimate.

Table A4.5.   50% construction-stage risk register

Risk no.	Residual risk	Probability	Severity of financial consequence	Mitigation action already undertaken	Further mitigation action
R1	Archaeological				
R1.1	Archaeological feature discovered on culvert route	2%	Level 3	Desk study has not revealed evidence of features apart from mine workings. Watching brief over most sensitive part of site has not revealed significant finds	Continue with archaeological watching brief to identify features at the earliest stage and contingency plans for action on discovery
R2	Environmental				
R2.1	Ground contamination levels substantially higher than predicted	3%	Level 4	Main and secondary ground investigations carried out to establish ground contamination levels. Ongoing testing has not revealed unexpected levels of contamination	
R2.2	Pollution of stream, and hence beach from contaminated ground	4%	Level 3	Approach agreed with EA Water Quality Officer. Method statements agreed and followed by the contractor to date	Continued vigilance by contractor and site staff to ensure compliance with specification
R2.3	Pollution of beach from general construction work			Standard EA clauses 1.14.1 to 7. Included in specification. Water quality monitored. Method statements agreed and followed by the contractor to date	Continued vigilance by contractor and site staff to ensure compliance with specification

Table A4.5.   continued

R2.4	Pollution of beach from general construction work			Specification restricted working area on the beach and controlled beach operations. Method statements agreed and followed by the contractor to date	
R2.5	Landfill tax: some material on site is discovered which is 'active' waste and therefore attracts a higher rate of tax	2%	Level 4	Waste regulator agreed rate of applicable based on ground investigation results	
R3	Dewatering				
R3.1	Dewatering fails to operate effectively			Ground investigation report gave contractor details of ground conditions and therefore appropriate dewatering techniques. Techniques have worked satisfactory to date	
R3.2	Dewatering causes property settlement and damage to services	5%	Level 2	Approximate zone of influence for dewatering determined to assess number of properties that could be affected. Specification for dewatering minimised risk of settlement. Pre-construction property survey undertaken	Site staff to continue to carefully monitor proposed method statements to minimise settlement

Table A4.5. continued

Risk no.	Residual risk	Probability	Severity of financial consequence	Mitigation action already undertaken	Further mitigation action
R3.3	Higher rates of dewatering required because soil is of higher permeability than predicted	1%	Level 3	Ground investigation results gave contractor details of soil permeability. No significant difference from SI to date	
R4	Mine workings				
R4.1	Mine workings discovered during construction	6%	Level 3	Culvert routed away from known mineshafts. Specify contractor to have procedures to note and act on warning signs. One shaft found to date, area of principal risk covered	
R4.2	Mineshaft collapses (due to increased water flow from dewatering, excavation or construction vibration)	1%	Level 2	As above	
R4.3	Multiple mineshaft collapses	0·5%	Level 1	As above	
R5	Damage to properties				
R5.1	Damage due to adjacent properties where excavating in close proximity	20%	Level 3	Works designed to minimise work near properties. Pre-construction property surveys undertaken. Methods being closely monitored	

Table A4.5. continued

R6	Flooding				
R6.1	Severe flooding, beyond what a contractor might reasonably expect	3%	Level 3	Analysis of flood frequency carried out. Highest risk period now passed	
R7	Compensation				
R7.1	Increase in compensation claims, principally due to extended working in Tywarnhale Square	Triangular distance about £25 000 upper=£55 000 lower=£5000	Level 3	Delays minimised	Minimise any further delays. EA Estates negotiate down claims
R8	Remeasurement				
R8.1	Remeasurement variation	Triangular distance about £0 upper=£18 000 lower=£ − 5000	Level 3	Accurate and ongoing measurement	Continue ongoing measurement to give advance warning of out-turn.

Note:
- Table to be read in conjunction with risk cost-estimation table (Table A4.2).
- Probability and financial consequence are given for the medium-risk case (see Table A4.2 for definition). Financial consequences which are the contractor's risk are zero rated.
- Financial consequences are divided into the following bands: VL: 0–£5000, L: £5000–£10 000, M: £10 000–£100 000, H: £100 000–£500 000, VH: >£500 000.
- 'Usual' construction risks, i.e. risks inherent in any large flood-defence project such as delays due to a site accident, have not been included.
- All mitigation actions are the responsibility of the consultant to specify in contract documents and the contractor to carry out on-site unless otherwise stated above.
- There are no significant secondary risks caused by the mitigation actions identified above.

Table A4.6.   50% construction-stage risk cost-estimation

Risk no.	Scenario	Probability	Description	Cost basis	Cost: £000s
R1.1	No event	92%			0
	Low	5%	Minor remains of little archaeological value or easily movable	1 day delay plus £1000 additional archaeological staff costs	8
	Medium	2%	More significant remains necessitating more extensive recording	6 day delay plus £10 000 archaeological investigation costs	52
	High	1%	Extensive remains of high archaeological value	4 month delay resulting in the need for contractor to demobilise/remobilize. £25 000 archaeological investigation costs	75
R2.1	No event	96·5%			0
	Low	2%	100 m^3 of spoil with > 1000 ppm arsenic requiring more stringent protective measures and disposal	Quote of additional £41 per m^3 above non-contaminated disposal costs (KS/PERR/26 18/1/96). Therefore £41–£15·6=£25·4 per m^3 more than used in appraisal report	2·5
	Medium	1%	300 m^3 with > 1000 ppm arsenic	Cost basis as above	7·5
	High	0·5%	1500 m^3 with > 1000 ppm arsenic	Cost basis as above	38
R2.2	No event	93%			0
	Low	4%	200 m^3 of beach sand has to be removed and placed	Allow £30 per m^3 for removal, disposal and importing correctly graded sand and placement	6
	Medium	2%	600 m^3 of beach sand has to be removed and placed	As above	18
	High	1%	1900 m^3 of beach sand has to be removed and placed	As above	57
R2.3	Do not evaluate as this is contractor's risk				

Table A4.6. continued

R2.4		Do not evaluate as this is contractor's risk			
R2.5	No event	96·5%			0
	Low	2%	50 m³ of spoil has to be reclassified as 'active waste'	Landfill Tax of £14 per m³ (increase of £10 per m³)	0·5
	Medium	1%	200 m³ of spoil has to be reclassified as 'active waste'	As above	2
	High	0·5%	1000 m³ of spoil has to be reclassified as 'active waste'	As above	10
R3.1		Do not evaluate as this is contractor's risk			
R3.2	No event	91·5%			0
	Low	5%	6 properties with minor cracking (requiring internal redecoration) and no service disruption	Allow £10 000 per property for internal redecoration and compensation	60
	Intermediate	2%	10 properties with minor cracking, 1 property with major cracking (requiring internal decoration and external re-rendering) and minor repairs	£10 000 per property for minor cracking. £40 000 for major cracking and £5000 for service repairs	145
	Medium	1%	12 properties with minor cracking and 2 properties with major cracking. Minor service repairs	A. N. Other's estimate of cost of works including compensation (memo of 28/5/96) and £10 000 allowance for servicing repairs	230
	High	0·5%	As above and also one property suffers severe cracking and has to be rebuilt. More major service repairs	Extrapolation of the above allowing £180 000 for rebuilding and including £50 000 allowance for service repairs	450
R3.3	No event	98·4%			0
	Low	1%	Soil permeability is an order of magnitude higher than anticipated over 10% of the route	Increase estimate of dewatering costs by 10%, i.e.10% of £160 000. Includes allowance for delay	16

Table A4.6.   continued

Risk no.	Scenario	Probability	Description	Cost basis	Cost: £000s
	Medium	0·5%	Soil permeability is an order of magnitude higher than anticipated over 30% of the route	Increase estimate of dewatering costs by 30%, i.e. 30% of £160 000. Includes allowance for delay	48
	High	0·1%	Soil permeability is an order of magnitude higher than anticipated over 60% of the route	Increase estimate of dewatering costs by 60%, i.e. 60% of £160 000. Includes allowance for delay	96
R4.1	No event	95%			0
	Low	3%	Shaft upstream-end of works where there are high rock levels	Capping works, no services damaged, no property damage and no delay	2·5
	Medium	0%	Shaft in area of playing fields or Boscawen Gardens, away from property	Capping works, minor service damage, no property damage and half a day delay	8
	High	2%	Shaft in downstream section adjacent to properties or adjacent to Boscawen Gardens properties	Capping works, £10 000 for services repair, £50 000 for property repairs/ compensation and 2 day delay	82
R4.2	No event	97·5%			0
	Low	0·5%	Shaft fails in upstream end of works away from properties	As R4.1 medium case	8
	Medium	1·5%	Shaft fails nearer properties	As R3.2 medium case plus 2 day delay	244
	High	0·5%	Shaft fails near properties. One property requires rebuilding	As R3.2 high case plus demobilisation/ remobilization costs	500
R4.3	No event	99·7%			0
	Low	0·2%	2 shafts fail in the upstream end of the works away from properties	2 times R4.2 low case	16

Table A4.6.   continued

	Medium	0·1%	2 shafts fail. 3 properties have to be rebuilt	3 times R3.2 high case plus demobilisation/ remobilization costs	1400
	High	0%	3 shafts fail in a densely built up area. 6 properties have to be rebuilt	6 times R3.2 2 high case plus demobilisation/ remobilization costs	2750
R5.1	No event	59%			0
	Low	25%	2 properties with minor cracking	A third of R3.2 low case	20
	Medium	12%	1 major cracking, additional underpinning works and 1 day delay	£40 000 for major cracking plus delay costs	47
	High	4%	1 property fails, rebuild and 2 day delay	£180 000 for rebuilding plus delay costs	194
R6.1	No event	95·2%	Flood event < 1 in 5-year		0
	Low	3%	1 in 10-year event	Loss of material and 1 day delay	12
	Medium	1·5%	1 in 25-year event	Loss of material, minor damage to plant and 2 day delay	30
	High	0·3%	1 in 50-year event	Loss of material, damage to plant and delay	80
R7.1	N/A	Triangular distance about £0 upper=£18 000 lower=£ − 5000	Risk of higher than anticipated compensation claims arising. Principally from delays in Tywarnhale Square	Estimates and likelihood from Colin Waugh	
R8.1	N/A	Triangular distance about £0 upper=£18 000 lower=£ − 5000	Risk of variation in construction remeasurement		

Note:
- Table to be read in conjunction with design-stage risk register (Table A4.1)
- Scenario definition:

No event	self explanatory
Low	low-cost scenario (given that a significant event has occurred)
Intermediate	cost between low and medium scenarios
Medium	medium-cost scenario
High	highest-cost scenario

Table A4.7.   Estimated out-turn costs at the 50% completion stage

Engineer's estimate item	Engineer's estimate: £	Currently approved estimate: £	Committed expenditure to 31/3/98: £	Final out-turn: £
1. Ground investigation	13 000	13 000	12 931	12 931
2. Archaeological watching brief	2000	2000	3000	6000*
Preliminary investigations	15 000	15 000	15 931	18 931
3–35 and 38–41 Engineering works	1 287 183	1 287 183	1 000 000	1 400 000[†]
37. Dealing with services: S.W.Water	87 500	87 000	10 000	10 000
SWEB			30 000	30 000
Engineering works	1 374 683	1 503 683	1 040 000	1 440 000[†]
42. Land purchases	54 000	54 000		54 000
43. Purchase Lupin Cottage	29 950	29 950		29 950
36. Demolition Lupin Cottage	5000	5000		4000
Land purchase	88 950	88 950		87 950
44. General compensation	132 000	132 000		132 000
45. Lost car-parking	8000	8000		8000
Compensation	140 000	140 000		140 000
46. Staff costs	45 000	45 000		40 000
47. Appraisal costs	90 000	90 000	90 914[‡]	90 914[‡]
48. Detailed design contract, documentation and admin.	108 000	108 000	109 272[‡]	125 604[‡]
49. Land agent negotiations	34 000	34 000		34 000
50. Site supervision costs	40 500	40 500	41 800[‡]	80 100[‡]
51. Environmental watching brief	1500	1500		0
52. Surface water: CCC	16 000	16 000		16 000
53. Surface water: S.W. Water	4000	4000		4000
Total other costs	294 000	294 000		350 618
MAFF LDWI estimate total	1 957 633	2 086 633		2 077 499
54. Risk items (50 percentile)	178 000	178 000		52 466
EA PID estimated total	2 135 633	2 264 633		2 129 965

* Tender £11 970 00
[†] Bolenna Fields — detailed landscaping to be added
[‡] Including Planning Supervisor costs

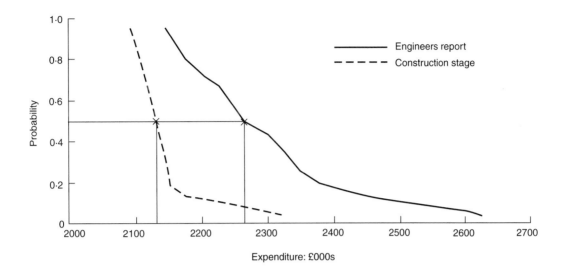

Figure A4.8. Probability cost distribution (in comparison to original curve) at the 50% completion stage

A4.9. PROJECT COMPLETION RISK ASSESSMENT

Unfortunately no data were available for the project completion case at the time of publication of this manual, however, feedback from the project team confirmed that the project was completed successfully and that costs were within anticipated limits.

A4.10. CONCLUSIONS AND RECOMMENDATIONS

It was clear (for this project) that *all* members of the project team considered application of the methodology beneficial. Not only was the project completed successfully with costs within anticipated limits, but also that the process encouraged openness and helped to promote a team-working atmosphere.

Specific benefits identified:

- A methodical, open and traceable process for considering and identifying project risks at the design stage — *confirming sound project feasibility that would give assurance throughout the project.*
- Provision of a more detailed estimate of potential project costs — *confirming that the project was acceptable to the client (given limited resources and including the risk of additional costs).*
- Clear identification of risks and appropriate mitigation measures for the construction stage. This removal of practical and foreseeable risk at source, along with mitigation measures where risk could not be completely removed, reduced the potential for unexpected events occurring, and hence the potential

for disagreement between parties. This led to an improved working relationship and teamworking on site. For example, discovery of unknown mine workings was taken as a routine part of the project rather than an issue for contention. *Improved teamworking through careful planning to cope with all potential risks and hence a reduction in the likelihood of disagreement and claims.*

- Ongoing monitoring of actual costs and potential risks — *improved understanding of financial risk.*

While for this particular study, the methodology was applied and undertaken on behalf of the client, it was clear that all parties of the project benefited. The process improved understanding and planning of the potential project risks, so promoting teamworking and the responsible sharing of responsibility for successful project completion.

This successful application of risk management techniques points to a change in working culture towards partnering/teamworking that has demonstrated value for all team members.

Appendix 5.
River and estuary engineering prompt lists

A5.1. RISK PROMPT LISTS

The following information is intended to aid risk identification and is focussed on river and estuary issues. It is not intended to offer an exhaustive list of risks but merely to prompt ideas. The information has been presented in two formats. Firstly, a list that contains words or phrases likely to prompt thought or discussion around risk issues for a project (Table A5.1). Secondly, a number of tables listing likely hazards, consequences and impacts for typical river engineering tasks or situations (Tables A5.2–A5.6). Possible risk mitigation measures are also offered.

Table A5.1. Single-word prompt list — river and estuary engineering

Risk item	Comments
Access	
Adjacent property	
Angling	
Archaeology	
Bank protection	
Bank stability	
Barges	
Beach	
Bed material	
Boats	
Breach	
Bridge	
Buried services	
Canoes	
Cofferdams	
Confined spaces	
Contamination	
Corrosion	
Currents	
Dam	
Debris	
Deposition	
Divers	
Docks	
Drainage	
Dredging	
Drowning	
Landowners	
Electricity	
Embankment	
Environment	
Explosion	

Table A5.1.   continued

Fire	
Fish	
Fishermen	
Flood defences	
Flood flows	
Flood level	
Flood warning	
Flooding	
Ground conditions	
Groundwater	
Harbour	
Hydrology	
Ice	
Life saving equipment	
Locks	
Modelling	
Mooring	
Navigation	
Piling	
Plant	
Pollution	
Pontoon	
Public access	
Public relations	
Pumps	
Rock	
Running sand	
Sand	
Scour	
Seasonal variations	
Sediment	
Services	

Table A5.1.   continued

Risk item	Comments
Silt	
Site access	
Site drainage	
Sluices	
Stability of floating plant	
Structure stability	
Super elevation	
Surge	
Swimming	
Terrorism	
Tides	
Timescale	
Tunnels	
Turbidity	
Vandalism	
Water levels	
Waves	
Weather	
Weirs	
Wildfowl	

Table A5.2. Environmental conditions that contribute to risk

| Hazard/problem | | Consequences | Potential impact on site | | Risks mitigation measures | Typical operations that are affected |
General	Specific		Primary impact	Secondary impact		
High river flows or river floods	Strong currents	Access difficult or impossible Difficult placing of structures and materials Difficult positioning of plant and materials Difficult working conditions Erosion of materials and structural foundations Inaccurate placing of structures and materials Loss of floating plant control Movement of structures prior to final anchoring Navigation and mooring hazardous or impossible Transport and handling of materials and plant difficult	Blockage of river by material and plant Damage to structures, plant and materials Environmental damage Suspension of work HSE/MCA enforcement action Injury or loss of life Loss of material Spillage of fuel Structure undermined	Blockage of river Environmental damage Suspension of work HSE/MCA enforcement action Land flooding Navigation Original design not achieved Partial failure of structure Pollution Third party impact	Adequate design of foundation and structure Analysis and specification of acceptable working conditions Navigation restrictions Programming work to minimise exposure of weak materials Restriction in flow Schedule work with tides Timing of works within appropriate seasons Use of flood-warning system	Closure of barrage Construction inside cofferdam Construction of bank protection Construction of cofferdam Construction of jetty decks Erection of pile guide frame Harbour wall deck casting Inspections by divers Material and plant delivery — by water Material and plant delivery — by road Piling — plant on land Piling — plant on water Placing of material — by plant on water Placing of materials — general Sinking caisson in place Towing of caissons to site Temporary cutting through existing sea defences
	High water-levels	Access road underwater Navigation under bridges impossible Plant/material washed into river	Plant and materials delivery problems Loss of plant and material Flooding of land	Potential for worsening of flood levels	Flood protection Flood-warning system Assessment of tide surge plus storm surges during construction	
	High water table	Access road muddy	Access difficult or impossible	Potential for worsening of flood levels	Flood protection Flood-warning system	
	Excessive forces on temporary works	Supporting frame damaged or lost	Blockage of river Environmental damage Work damaged	Land flooding Third party impact	Flood action plan Flood-forecasting system	

Table A5.2. *continued*

Hazard/problem		Consequences	Potential impact on site		Risks mitigation measures	Typical operations that are affected
General	Specific		Primary impact	Secondary impact		
	Excessive forces on incomplete works	Damage and/or collapse of works Overtopping of works	Damage to structures, plant, and materials Injury or loss of life	Suspension of work HSE/MCA enforcement action Land flooding Loss of material Navigation Third party impact	Evacuation procedures for personnel Flood-warning system Suitable-designed temporary works Timing of works within appropriate seasons Weather forecasting	
	Impact from floating trash	Damage of works	Blockage of river Environmental damage		Schedule work with tides Protective dolphins and fenders with navigation marks Use of protective boom	
Tidal conditions	Periodic low water	Navigation and mooring impossible	Beaching of plant			Closure of barrage Construction inside cofferdam Construction of bank protection Construction of cofferdam Construction of jetty decks Harbour wall deck casting Material and plant delivery — by water Placing of materials Piling — plant on water Sinking caisson in place Towing of caissons to site
	Strong currents	Access not possible Difficult handling and placing of materials Difficult working conditions Erosion of materials and structural foundations Injury or loss of life Loss of floating plant control Transport impossible	Blockage of river Environmental damage Navigation and mooring hazardous	Land flooding Navigation Third party impact	Flood-warning system Programming work to minimise exposure of weak materials Timing of works within appropriate seasons	
	Flooding of completed chambers Restricted working height	Permanent works and equipment damaged by flooding Workforce trapped, injured or drowned Damage and/or collapse of structure	Blockage of river Damage to equipment or works Environmental damage Suspension of work	Land flooding Partial failure of structure Third party impact	Allow flow through sluice or locks Careful sealing of machinery chambers Strict control of personnel working below deck	

Hazard	Cause	Consequence	Effect	Further effect	Control measures	Activities
			HSE/MCA enforcement action; Injury or loss of life; Loss of plant and material; Structure undermined		Work schedule planned between tides; Weather forecast/tide/surge prediction system	
	Excessive external forces	Collapse of structure	Damage to structures, plant and materials; Injury or loss of life	Suspension of work; HSE/MCA enforcement action; Land flooding	Adequate temporary condition design; Evacuation procedures for personnel; Flood and weather forecasting	
	Impact floating debris		Blockage of river; Environmental damage		Protective dolphins and fenders with navigation marks; Timing of works within appropriate seasons	
Wave conditions	Severe wave action	Difficult working conditions; Loss of floating plant control; Transport impossible	Blockage of river; Environmental damage; Navigation and mooring impossible; Spillage of fuel	Land flooding; Navigation; Pollution; Third party impact	Design of structure; Timing of transport; Wave-prediction system; Weather forecasting	Erection of pile guide frame; Construction inside cofferdam; Construction of bank protection; Construction of cofferdam; Construction of jetty decks; Handling of material; Harbour-wall deck casting

Table A5.2. *continued*

Hazard/problem		Consequences	Potential impact on site		Risks mitigation measures	Typical operations that are affected
General	Specific		Primary impact	Secondary impact		
						Material and plant delivery — by water Placing of material — by plant on water Placing of materials — general Piling — plant on water Towing of caissons to site
	Flooding of works	Damage to works Collapse of works	Blockage of river Damage to structures, plant and materials Environmental damage Injury or loss of life	Suspension of work HSE/MCA enforcement action Land flooding Third party impact	Consideration of wave climate in temporary works design	
	Strong currents	Difficult handling and placing of materials Difficult working conditions Erosion of materials and structural foundations	Loss of material or structure		Timing of works within appropriate seasons	
	Excessive forces on guiding frame	Guiding frame damaged Guiding frame lost in river	Blockage of river Environmental damage	Land flooding Navigation Third party impact	Flood-forecasting system	

	Excessive forces on incomplete works Impact of floating debris	Damage to works Collapse of works	Injury or loss of life	Partial failure Suspension of work HSE/MCA enforcement action	Adequate temporary works design Wave prediction	Construction generally
Wind conditions	Plant operation	Handling of plant and materials Wave forces apply	Damage to temporary works Loss of materials	Damage of works Environmental damage	Restrict working during storm winds	Material and plant delivery — by water Material and plant delivery — by road Placing of material — by plant on water Piling — plant on water
Cold weather	Icy access road	Plant lost in river Material fallen into river	Loss of materials and plant		Use salts Surface protection	
	Ice covering river	Access impossible	Blockage of river		Weather forecasting	

Table A5.3. *Construction techniques that contribute to risk*

Hazard/problem		Consequences	Potential impact on site		Risks mitigation measures	Typical operations that are affected
General	Specific		Primary impact	Secondary impact		
Use of explosives		Damage to buildings or structures Environmental damage Injury from debris	Authorities preventing further use of explosives Injunctions from property owners or public Third party impact	Compensation to affected parties	Damage limitation measures (e.g. bunds, etc.) Use alternative method	Dredging of bed — removal of rock
Contaminated sediments		Release of pollutants	Environmental damage	Third party impact	Core samples prior to work commencement	Dredging of bed — removal of silt
Re-suspension of silt		Release of silt plume	Environmental damage	Third party impact	Damage limitation measures Use alternative measures	Dredging of bed — removal of silt
Use of unwashed material		Release of silt plume	Amenity Environmental damage	Third party impact	Wash material	Placing of material under water
Workforce working over water		Fall into water	Injury or loss of life	Suspension of work HSE/MCA enforcement action	Awareness of personnel Flood-warning system Protection and training for personnel Provision of safety boat Edge protection Clothing, buoyancy aids, etc.	Closure of barrage Construction of jetty Piling-plant on water

Launch site or construction dock	Unsuitable launch system. Inadequate water depth over construction dock sill	Structural damage, sinking or grounding of caisson	Blockage of river or dock		Careful planning of launch sequence and assessment of caisson draught at launch	Launch of structures into river or sea
Distortion of piles	Sheet piles becoming de-clutched after hitting obstruction during driving	Pile unable to carry design loading	Need to withdraw and re-drive piles	Pile damaged beyond repair	Careful monitoring of driving of piles especially if driving suddenly becomes very hard	Construction of cofferdam Piling
	Refusal of pile	Reduction in carrying capacity of tension pile	Re-design of structure required locally		Adequate site investigation	
Creation of an obstruction underwater		Increased water levels Navigation impaired	Land flooding Damage vessels		Checks by divers	Placing of material or structures
Trench side slopes too steep	Material causes failure	Buried trench collapse	Injury or loss of life Re-excavation required	Suspension of work HSE/MCA enforcement action	River or seabed material investigation	Trenching underwater
Insufficient support of excavation	Instability of excavation	Trench collapse	Injury or loss of life Re-excavation required	Suspension of work HSE/MCA enforcement action	Adequate support of trench Check site investigation prior to construction starting	Trenching on land

Table A5.4. Plant and material selections that contribute to risk

| Hazard/problem | | Consequences | Potential impact on site | | Risks mitigation measures | Typical operations that are affected |
General	Specific		Primary impact	Secondary impact		
Noise from plant		Excess noise	Environmental damage	Third party impact	Bunds and/or acoustic screens Use of silent plant Limits on working hours Visual impact	Piling — plant on land Temporary pumping arrangements
Vibration from plant		Excess ground vibration	Structural stability of adjacent properties, works and bank		Selection of plant Structural survey	Piling — plant on land
Plant operation	Dredger Excavator	Destruction of river environment	Environmental damage	Third party impact	Consultation prior to construction works Planning of works with correct plant and equipment	Cutting of new channel
Damage of cables	Services Hawsers	Interruption of site services supply	Injury or loss of life Injury or loss of life	Suspension of work HSE/MCA enforcement action	Define risk area around services Avoid use of steel wire ropes	Cutting of new channel Towing of pipes
Handling of pipes		Personnel working in trench hit by pipe Damage to pipe	Injury or loss of life Loss of primary material	Suspension of work HSE/MCA enforcement action	Control of lay barge Follow instructions of banksman	Laying pipes in river Trenching on land
Flows at pump	Strong currents created at inlet and outlet	Fish sucked into pumps Navigation hazard Re-suspension of mobile sediment Swimmers injured or killed by pump	Environmental damage Injury or loss of life	Suspension of work HSE/MCA enforcement action	Install pump-suction protection Restrict public access Use of warning signs	Construction of river diversion — pumped system Sluice inlet and outlets

River flow excessive	Design flow not known	Size of pump insufficient	Flooding of land and works		Assessment of river flow prior to installation of temporary works	Construction of river diversion — pumped system
Unsuitable material	Inadequate long-term chemical and physical durability Incorrect rock shape Incorrect size or grading of rock	Loss of stability under wave attack Reduced safe working-life	Early local failure of sections of structure	Need for local repairs	Rigorous supervision in quarry and at construction site Use of standard grading and/or specification	Handling of material with crane
Slippage of material stock piles	Excessive surcharge adjacent to river bed/ excavation Insufficient bearing capacity of ground under stockpile	Collapse of bank or works Material contamination with soil and water	Plant/personnel buried Works/material damaged	Suspension of work HSE/MCA enforcement action	Careful siting of stockpiles and consideration of ground properties and loading	Construction process Material delivery

Table A5.5. *External influences that contribute to risk*

| Hazard/problem | | Consequences | Potential impact on site | | Risks mitigation measures | Typical operations that are affected |
General	Specific		Primary impact	Secondary impact		
Environmentally sensitive area		Loss of amenity	Environmental damage	Third party impact	Apply damage limitation measures (booms, etc.) Use alternative site	Material and plant delivery
Other river users	Trespass into working areas	Interference with operation	Danger to life and operations Risk of vandalism and theft		Clear identification of working areas	Material and plant delivery Installation of structures
	Navigation	Collision with other boats	Blockage to river by material and barge Damage to barge and material Damage to structures, banks and boats Injury or loss of life Spillage of fuel	Suspension of work HSE/MCA enforcement action Pollution Third party impact	Advance warning of works Clear identification of working area Restrict navigation Use of tugs/local pilots	
Location of river	Fall into river	Plant and material in water	Blockage of river by plant and material Damage to plant and material Spillage of fuel	Blockage to river Suspension of work HSE/MCA enforcement action Pollution Third party impact	Awareness of drivers Careful design of access road (alignment, material, protection of banks, signals)	Construction of barrage Construction of jetty Material and plant delivery — by road alongside river
	High water table	Poor ground conditions	Access difficult	Mud carried in surrounding area Visual impact	Careful design of temporary access road Surface protection Timing of delivery	

Third party access rights	Right of way interacting with access route	Third parties close to works area	Danger to life and operation		Diversion of public rights of way Clear identification of site and access	Construction of river diversion Cutting of new river channel Material and plant delivery — by road alongside river
	Vandalism to plant	Interference with operation Damage to plant Spillage of fuel	Damage to life and operations Risk of theft Environmental damage	Flooding of land and works Third party impact Delays	Site security Back-up system Restrict public access	
Navigation	Danger to personnel	Divers hit by vessels	Injury or loss of life	Suspension of work HSE/MCA enforcement action	Awareness of divers Clear identification of working area Restrict navigation Use of fenders Use of signals	Checks by divers Construction inside cofferdam Erection of pile guide Piling
	Impact from vessels on structures	Collapse of structure Overtopping of structure	Blockage of river Damage to structures, banks and boats	Suspension of work HSE/MCA enforcement action Land flooding Navigation Third party impact	Design to resist impact Escape planning Flood forecasting Timing of works Weather forecasting	
Suitability of site	Insufficient bearing capacity for weight of structure	Differential settlement and/or structural damage	Re-design of structure		Careful assessment of soil conditions at construction site Possible need to move to alternative site	Construction of caissons Piling

Table A5.6. Unknown, uncontrollable and accidental influences that contribute to risk

Hazard/problem		Consequences	Potential impact on site		Risks mitigation measures	Operations that are affected
General	Specific		Primary impact	Secondary impact		
Insufficient anchoring	Tie force under-estimated	Collapse of anchors	Blockage of river Damage to structures Environmental damage	Third party impact	Ensure adequate safety factor in design	Backfilling
	Anchor points incorrectly located	Failure of anchors			Check on construction setting out	
Permanent reduction or loss of stability	Soft material, e.g. silt not removed before placing granular fill	Complete failure of structure	Blockage to river Environment damage		Rigorous site control including close inspection of foundation	Backfilling Piling
	Unsuitable fill material of low angle of internal friction	Partial or complete collapse			Select suitable material for design	
Liquefac-tion of foundation		Collapse of structure	Blockage of river Damage to structures Environmental damage	Land flooding Navigation Third party impact	Design structure with adequate appreciation of seepage flows under toe of the piles up into structure	Dewatering of cofferdam Construction of a weir

Hazard	Cause	Event	Effect	Consequence	Control measures	Activity
Failure of pump	Accidental	Flooding of land and works	Damage to structure or works		Arrange duty and standby pumps; Monitor operation of pumps	Construction of river diversion
	Blockage	Cavitation of pump	Failure of temporary works	Land flooding	Ensure trash screens are fitted	
Buried services	Plant damage to existing services	Interruption of services; Injury or loss of life	Failure of site services; Disruption to third party; Work suspended	Third party impact	Ensure plant operators are prudent when warning markers are found; Mark and record all known services	Cutting new river channel; Site establishment; Transplanting of trees
Blockage of river	Trash	Increase water levels	Land flooding	Third party impact	Monitor works for trash	Construction of cofferdam
	Fish unable to pass obstruction	Fish unable to feed	Environmental damage		Transport fish artificially	General operations
River flood		Flooding of new channel before its completion; Scour of cutting; Overtopping of cofferdam	Environmental damage; Sediment deposition downstream; Suspension of work	Navigation; Land flooding; Pumping-out cofferdam	Flood-warning system; Consider top level of cofferdam (subject to approval)	Cutting of new channel; Diversion of existing river
Unknown ground conditions	Obstructions to driving foundations	Driving difficult or impossible	Delays; Additional plant required; Environmental damage		Clearance of bed surface material; Selection of appropriate plant; Site investigation; Use of divers	Construction of cofferdam; Construction of permanent works
	Premature failure of structure	Collapse or damage to structure	Loss of structure		Site investigation	

Table A5.6. continued

Hazard/problem		Consequences	Potential impact on site		Risks mitigation measures	Operations that are affected
General	Specific		Primary impact	Secondary impact		
Navigation in diversion channel		Vessel impact	Injury or loss of life	Suspension of work HSE/MCA enforcement action Third party impact	Provide traffic control scheme Use of fenders	Construction of river diversion
River flows in diversion channel	Fast currents	Scour of bed and bank Raised groundwater levels	Deposition of sediment downstream Environmental damage	Third party impact	Protect bed and bank of diverted channel	Construction of river diversion
	Design flow unknown	Size of diverted channel insufficient	Flooding of land and works	Third party impact	Design temporary channel to accommodate adequate flow	

Appendix 6.
Additional health and safety information

This appendix contains further information and references (available at the time of publication) in the following three areas:

- Legislation — European directives, Acts and Regulations
- Safety
- Health.

Contact details for local and national HSE offices, MCA offices and MAIB.

A6.1. LEGISLATION

A6.1.1. European Directives

- The Framework Directive (89/391/EEC)
- Machinery Directive (89/392/EEC)
- Workplace Directive (89/654/EEC)
- Personal Protective Equipment Directive (89/656/EEC)
- Temporary or Mobile Sites Directive (92/57/EEC)
- Amending Directive to the Use of Work Equipment Directive (95/63/EC)

A6.1.2. Acts

Health and Safety at Work Act 1974 (HSWA)
The HSWA and its relevant statutory provisions apply to all work activities in Great Britain and to specified activities in British territorial waters and designated areas. There is separate legislation for Northern Ireland. The HSWA and its relevant statutory provisions, including the Docks Regulations 1988, cover the safety of shore-based personnel. These provisions also cover the safety of people who are not shore-based onboard ships, while they are in Great Britain and certain other activities while in territorial waters. The HSWA and its relevant statutory provisions cover the safety of anyone at work while they are in Great Britain and engaged in certain other activities in territorial waters. The HSWA also covers risks to others (i.e. the general public) arising from construction works. The HSWA does not apply to the master and crew of a sea-going ship or

their clients, in respect of the normal shipboard activities of a ship's crew, under the direction of the master.

Merchant Shipping Act 1995 (MSA)

The health and safety aspects of this Act apply to United Kingdom sea-going vessels (both in open sea and inland) wherever they may be and certain requirements apply to non-UK sea-going vessels while they are in UK territorial waters. It is generally compatible with the HSWA. The Act enables the Secretary of State for Transport to make regulations governing the safety of sea-going vessels and persons on them. The Act, and regulations made under it, covers among other things the safety of a sea-going vessels, its passengers and crew. In particular, merchant shipping health and safety regulations apply to all persons working onboard ship. Codes of Practice made under MSA apply to non sea-going vessels in commercial use, e.g. work boats, safety boats, floating cranes, etc.

A6.1.3. Regulations

The Management of Health and Safety at Work Regulations 1992 (MHSW)

The MHSW Regulations require that the risks associated with any hazardous work activity are assessed before work starts, so that necessary preventative and protective measures can be identified and put into place. The process of risk assessment should start at the design and planning stage of a project and continue during the construction phase. Workers must be competent to carry out their tasks, which may require instruction or training to understand, and also to implement, any control measures. Clients must monitor the workplace to ensure that any control measures are implemented and effective (including undertaking health surveillance, if necessary).

The Construction (Design and Management) Regulations 1994 (CDM)

The CDM Regulations places duties on all those involved in construction works, including clients, designers and contractors. The regulations require the client to appoint a Planning Supervisor and a competent Principal Contractor, as soon as practicable, to co-ordinate health and safety matters. The Planning Supervisor co-ordinates health and safety initially and the Principal Contractor co-ordinates it when the construction phase commences. Embedded in the regulations is a requirement for the designer to consider health and safety in the design and to co-operate with the Planning Supervisor and other designers.

The objective of CDM is to reduce the high accident-rate in the construction industry by causing those involved with construction projects to consider health and safety issues as a fundamental part of designing a new project — not only during construction, but throughout the whole life of the building or structure, so that it is easy and safe to maintain and modify, and eventually to demolish. CDM requires the creation of a health and safety plan (for construction) and, so that future builders and architects will know what they are dealing with, a health and safety file (for future construction works).

The Construction (Health, Safety and Welfare) Regulations 1996 (CHSW)
The CHSW Regulations consolidate, modernise and simplify the older requirements and introduce some important new provisions arising from the implementation of an EC Directive on construction. These Regulations complete the implementation of the Directive that was started by the introduction of CDM. The Regulations cover a wide range of hazards including many associated with river and estuary engineering including: safe places of work, cofferdams and caissons, prevention from drowning, traffic routes, emergency routes and exits, emergency procedures, welfare facilities, temperature and weather protection and lighting. Within the Regulations there are two areas that are particularly relevant to working within a river and estuary environment which are:

(a) *Excavations, cofferdams and caissons (Regulations 12 and 13)*
    (i)   Prevent collapse of ground both in and above excavations.
    (ii) Identify and prevent risk from underground cables and other services.
    (iii) Ensure cofferdams and caissons are properly designed, constructed and maintained.
    (iv) From the outset, and as work progresses, any excavation which has the potential to collapse unless supported, should have suitable equipment immediately available to provide such support.

(b) *Prevention or avoidance of drowning (Regulation 14)*
    (i)   Take steps to prevent people from falling into water or other liquid so far as is reasonably practicable.
    (ii) Ensure that personal protective and rescue equipment is immediately available for use and maintained, in the event of a fall.
    (iii) Make sure safe transport by water is under the control of a competent person.

The Docks Regulations 1988
These regulations apply to some aspects of construction work, particularly where equipment or materials are brought in by barge, etc. A dock operation means the loading or unloading of goods on or from a ship at dock premises and incidental activities, including the storing, sorting, inspecting, checking, weighing or handling of goods; the movement of goods, passengers and vehicles; the use of welfare amenities in relation to those activities. It includes loading from one ship to another when both are moored at a buoy. Dock premises mean any dock or other place at which ships load or unload goods, neighbouring land or water which is used and any part of a ship when so used.

Dangerous Substances in Harbour Areas Regulations 1987 (DSHAR)
Statutory harbour authorities are responsible for enforcing certain provisions of the DSHAR including those relating to the entry of dangerous goods into harbour areas and the marking and navigation of vessels.

In addition, many harbour authorities have powers to regulate in their area of control by bye-laws, and may do so. Such bye-laws are without prejudice to the requirements of DSHAR etc. Private Harbour Acts may contain provisions or enabling powers (e.g. to make bye-laws) which may also overlap with HSWA. The DSHAR is due to be replaced shortly by the Dangerous Goods in Harbour Areas Regulations which are presently at the consultation stage.

(These Regulations are to be replaced by the Dangerous Goods in Harbour Areas Regulations)

The Provision and Use of Work Equipment Regulations 1998 (PUWER)

PUWER provides guidance on the safeguarding of machinery and work equipment, controls and control-systems markings and warning signs. They implement the non-lifting aspects of the Amending Directive to the Use of Work Equipment Directive 95/63/EC (AUWED).

The Lifting Operations and Lifting Equipment Regulations 1998 (LOLER)

These Regulations implement the lifting aspects of the AUWED and replace the lifting equipment provisions of the Factories Act 1961 and several provisions contained in industry specific regulations, including those relating to safe work at docks and in shipbuilding within confined spaces (Regulations and guidance 1997). LOLER Regulation 6 applies to the positioning and installation of any crane and LOLER Regulation 8 applies to the organisation of the lifting operation.

LOLER defines confined spaces and the dangers which can arise within them and details checks to be made before entering confined spaces, methods of ventilation, special tools and lighting, communications and emergency procedures.

Personal Protective Equipment at Work Regulations 1992 (PPEWR)

PPEWR considers provision and use of personal protective-equipment, including safety helmets, ear defenders, eye protection, clothing, boots and gloves.

PUWER and LOLER do not apply to work or lifting equipment on ships (where merchant shipping legislation applies), but in operations where there is a risk to shore-based workers a shore employer must satisfy himself that the merchant shipping requirements in respect of the equipment are being complied with. A ship is defined as 'every vessel used in navigation' and includes items such as floating cranes used at waterside construction sites.

A6.2. HEALTH AND SAFETY

Guidance on many construction-related health and safety issues is provided by the HSE in the form of notes, guides or books. The guidance notes provide outline advice and often refer to more detailed documents or guides that have been produced. There are considerably more references relevant to general construction works. The HSE produce several summary documents that list documents, namely:

- HSE books — a list of free publications
- HSE books — price list
- safety culture — a clear guide to the HSE publications most likely to be needed
- videos from the HSE.

For further information contact the HSE Information Centre (for contact details see Section A6.3).

A6.2.1. Safety

Outlined below is a list of references for further guidance on various safety topics.

Working over/adjacent to water
- HSE. *Working over water.* Regulation 14, CHSW Regulations, 1996.
- HSE. *Health and Safety in construction*, 1996.
- Construction Industry Training Board (CITB). *Construction site safety notes. No. 30 GE 700//30. Working over water*, 1992.
- Building Employers' Confederation (BEC). *Construction safety, Section 8E Working over water*, 1988.
- CIRIA Special Publication 130. *Site safety*, 1997.
- CIRIA Special Publication 57. *Handling materials on site*, 1988.
- BS 8083:1991. *Code of practice for the use of safety nets, containment nets and sheets on constructional works.*
- CIRIA Special Publication 57. *Handling materials on site.*
- CIRIA Special Publication 137. *Site safety for the water industry.*
- *Buoyancy equipment on inland and inshore waters* (Agricultureal Information Sheet No. 1). This gives details of personal buoyancy equipment and its care and maintenance. The types of buoyancy equipment most appropriate for use at waterside construction sites are:

  - BS EN 396:1994. *Lifejackets and personal buoyancy aids: Lifejackets: 150N.* These have a buoyancy of no less than 150 Newtons for the average adult and are intended for use in tidal waters or when foul weather clothing is being used; and where the wearers may not be capable of helping themselves due to injury or exhaustion (or where there may be a delay in rescue).
  - BS EN 399:1994. *Lifejackets and personal buoyancy aids: Lifejackets: 275N.* These have a buoyancy of no less than 275 Newtons for the average adult and are intended for use in tidal waters in extreme conditions, when heavy protective clothing is being worn or loads such as tool belts are being carried; and where the wearers may not be capable of helping themselves due to injury or exhaustion (or where there may be a delay in rescue).
  - BS EN 394:1994. *Lifejackets and personal buoyancy aids: Additional items.* This standard deals with emergency lights, safety harnesses, protective covers, etc.

Cofferdams

- CIRIA Special Publication 95. *The design and construction of sheet piled cofferdams.*

Earth moving plant

- HSE. *Working over water.* Regulation 14, CHSW Regulations, 1996.
- Building Employers' Confederation (BEC). *Construction safety, Section 8E Working over water,* 1988.

Sea outfalls

- CIRIA Special Publication 158. *Sea outfalls — inspection and diver safety.*

Diving

- The Stationery Office (1997). *The Diving at Work Regulations 1997/2776.*
- HSE Books (1998). *Commercial diving projects offshore. The Diving at Work Regulations 1997. Approved Code of Practice and guidance — L103.*
- HSE Books (1998). *Commercial diving projects inland/inshore. The Diving at Work Regulations 1997. Approved Code of Practice and guidance — L104.*
- HSE Books (1998). *Recreational diving projects. The Diving at Work Regulations 1997. Approved Code of Practice and guidance — L103.*
- HSE Books (1998). *Media diving projects. The Diving at Work Regulations 1997. Approved Code of Practice and guidance — L106.*
- HSE Books (1998). *Scientific and archaeological diving projects. The Diving at Work Regulations 1997. Approved Code of Practice and guidance — L107.*
- The International Marine Contractors Association issues a number of guidance notes which are available from: IMCA, Carlyle House, 235 Vauxhall Bridge Road, London, SW1V 1EJ.
- The Association of Diving Contractors issues a number of guidance notes which are available from: ADC, Carlyle House, 235 Vauxhall Bridge Road, London, SW1V 1EJ.

Explosives underwater

- *Guidelines for the safe use of explosives underwater.* MTD Publication 96/101. The Marine Technology Directorate Ltd, 1996.
- *Establishing exclusion zones when using explosives in demolition.* (Construction Information Sheet No. 45.)

A6.2.1. Health

The following list includes HSE guidance notes relevant to health issues when working in the river and estuary environment.

Business

- *Good Health is Good Business,* 1998.
- *Provision of welfare facilities at transient construction sites.* (Construction Information Sheet No. 46.)

- *Construction (Design and Management) Regulations 1994; The role of the Designer* (Construction Information Sheet No. 41.)
- *Construction (Design and Management) Regulations 1994; The Health and Safety Plan during the construction phase.* (Construction Information Sheet No. 43.)
- *Construction health and safety checklist.* (Construction Information Sheet No. 17.)
- *Provision of welfare facilities at fixed construction sites.* (Construction Information Sheet 18.)

Diving
- *Are you involved in a diving project?*

Physical
- *Getting to grips with manual handling,* 1999.

Environment
- *Safe work in confined spaces,* 1997.
- *Oxygen, fire and explosion hazards,* 1992.
- *Keeping your top on — health risks from working in the sun,* 1998.
- *Offshore first aid,* 1994.
- *How HSE assesses offshore safety cases,* 1997.
- *Offshore health and safety legislation,* 1998.
- *Health and Safety on floating fish farm installations,* 1997.
- *Working with sewage,* 1997.
- *Biological monitoring in the workplace,* 1997.
- *Construction fire safety.* (Construction Information Sheet No. 51).
- *Noise in construction.*

Materials
- *Cobalt and you,* 1995.
- *Lead and You,* 1998.
- *Skin cancer caused by oil,* 1998.
- *Preventing dermatitis at work,* 1997.
- *Interpreting biocide,* 1991.
- *Chemical cleaners.* (Construction Information Sheet 24.)
- *Cement.* (Construction Sheet 26.)
- *Solvents.* (Construction Information Sheet 27.)
- *Silica.* (Construction Information Sheet 36.)

Infection
- *Leptospirosis (Weils Disease),* 1996.

A6.3 Contact details for local and national HSE offices, MCA offices and MAIB

Organisation	Telephone	Fax
HSE Information Centre Broad Lane Sheffield, S3 7HQ www.open.gov.uk/hse/hsehome.htm	0541-545-500	
HSE Safety Policy Division Rose Court 2 Southwark Bridge London, SE1 9HS	020-7717-6000 Marine 020-7717-6211 Offshore 020-7717-6722 Diving 020-7717-6592	020-7717-6699 020-7717-6908 020-7717-6680
HSE/OSD Lord Cullen House Fraser Place Aberdeen, AB9 1UB	01224-252500	01224-252555 01224-252577 01224-252629 or 01224-252549
HSE 122A Thorpe Road Norwich, NR1 1RN	0160-275000	0160-275050 or 0160-275055
HSE/CHID (Pipelines) Aberdeen and Norwich as above *Attention* Principal Pipelines Inspector	as above	
HSE/OSD Merton House Stanley Road Liverpool, L20 3DL	0151-951-3157 or 0151-951-3107	0151-951-3158
HSE/FOD Room DH1011 Daniel House Stanley Precinct Bootle Merseyside, L20 7HE or Area Office	0151-951-4000 or 0151-951-4851 or Area Office	0151-951-4908 or 0151-951-4889
HSE/24 hours	0151-951-4000	
HSE Wales and West Region *Regional Office Wales* Brunel House 2 Fitzalan Road Cardiff, CF2 1SH	029-2026-3000	029-2026-3120 029-2026-3068
South-West Inter City House Mitchell Lane Victoria Street Bristol, BS1 6AN	01179-886000	01179-262998

Organisation	Telephone	Fax
South-West Ballard House West Hoe Road Plymouth, PL1 3BL	01752-668481	01752-226024
HSE Home Counties Region *Regional Office* 14 Cardiff Road Luton Bedfordshire, LU1 1PP	01582-444200	01582-444320
South Priestley House Priestly Road Basingstoke Hants, RG24 9NW	01256-404000	01256-404100
South 14 New Fields Stinsford Road Nuffield Industrial Estate Poole Dorset, BH17 7NF	01202-667219	01202-667224
East Anglia 39 Baddow Road Chelmsford Essex, CM2 0HL	0124-528-4661	0125-525-2633
East Anglia Kiln House Pottergate Norwich, NR2 1DA	01603-615711	01603-761436
HSE London and South-East Region *Regional Office* St Dunstan's House 201–211 Borough High Street Southwark London, SE1 1JA	020-7556-2100	020-7556-2200
South-East 3 East Grinstead House London Road East Grinstead West Sussex, RH19 1RR	01342-334200	01342-334222
South-East International House Dover Place Ashford Kent, TN23 1HU	01233-624658	01233-634827

Organisation	Telephone	Fax
HSE Midlands Region		
Regional Office McLaren Building 35 Dale End Birmingham, B4 7NP	0121-607-6200	0121-607-6349
North Midlands and Lincolnshire Birkbeck House Trinity Square Nottingham, NG1 4AU	0115-947-0712	0115-941-1577
HSE York and North-East Region		
Regional Office Woodside House 261 Low Lane Horsforth Leeds, LS18 5TW	0113-283-4200	0113-258-8029
South Yorkshire Sovereign House 110 Queen Street Sheffield, S1 2ES	0114-291-2300	0114-291-2379
South Yorkshire Festival House Jameson Street Hull, HU1 3JR	01482-223487	01482-218855
West and North Yorkshire 8 St Paul's Street Leeds, LS1 2LE	0113-283-4200	0113-283-4296
North-East Arden House Regent Centre Regent Farm Road Gosforth Newcastle-upon-Tyne, NE3 3JN	0191-202-6200	0191-202-6300
Regional Office — Merseyside The Triad Stanley Road Bootle Merseyside, L20 3PG	0151-479-2200	0151-479-2201
Greater Manchester Quay House Quay Street Manchester, M3 3JB	0161-952-8200	0161-952-8222

Organisation	Telephone	Fax
North-West Victoria House Ormskirk Road Preston, PR1 1HH	01772-259-321	01772-821-807
North-West 2 Victoria Place Carlisle Cumbria, CA1 1ER	01228-39321	01228-28282
HSE Scotland *Head Office — Scotland East* Belford House 59 Belford Road Edinburgh, EH14 3UE	0131-247-2000	0131-247-2121
Scotland West 375 West George Street Glasgow, G2 4LW	0141-275-3000	0141-275-3100
Scotland North East Lord Cullen House Fraser Place Aberdeen, AB9 1UB	01224-252500	01224-252525
Scotland North 28 Longman Road Inverness, IV1 1SF	01463-718101	01463-713459
Maritime and Coastguard Agency *Head and South of England Regional Office* Spring Place 105 Commercial Road Southampton, SO15 1EG	023-8032-9100 GTN 1513-100 or Regional Office 023-8032-9329 GTN 1513-329	023-8032-9251 023-8032-9351
London Central Court 1b Knoll Rise Orpington Kent, BR6 0JA	01689-890400	01689-890446
Falmouth Imperial Buildings Bar Road Falmouth Cornwall	01326-312761	01326-319399
Plymouth Phoenix House Notte Street Plymouth, PL1 2HF	01752-266211	01752-225826

Organisation	Telephone	Fax
Great Yarmouth 5th Floor Yarmouth House 45 Yarmouth Way Great Yarmouth Norfolk, NR30 2QZ	01493-330433	01493-330489
Swansea Tutt Head Mumbles Swansea West Glamorgan, SA3 4HW	01792-368472	01792-363125
Beverley North of England and Wales Regional Office Crosskill House Mill Lane Beverley Yorks, HU17 9JB	01482-866606	01482-869989
Stockton-on-Tees Middlesborough 3rd Floor, Victoria House Pearson Court Pearson Way Stockton-on-Tees 12-16 Woodlands Road Middlesborough Cleveland, TS17 6PT	01642-611040	01642-614048
Newcastle Government Buildings Broadway West Gosforth Newcastle-upon-Tyne, NE3 2JL	0191-285-7171 GTN 5217-171	0191-284-7464
Liverpool 2nd Floor Graeme House Derby Square Liverpool Merseyside, L2 7SQ	0151-471-1142	0151-471-1143
Cardiff 2nd Floor Oxford House Hills Street Cardiff, CF1 2TD	029-2022-9556	029-2022-9017
Milford Haven The Old Smoke House The Docks Milford Haven, SA73 2AF	01646-693272	01646-690137

Organisation	Telephone	Fax
MCA Aberdeen Scotland and Northern Ireland *Regional Office* Marine House Blaikies Quay Aberdeen, AB11 5EZ	01224-574122	01224-571920 (1st floor) 01224-573725 (3rd floor)
Glasgow 6000 Academy Park Gower Street Glasgow, G51 1TR	0141-427-9400	0141-427-9401
Belfast Customs House Queens Square Belfast, BT1 3EU	02890-562962 (via Customs and Excise switchboard)	02890-562960
Leith 1 Johns Place Leith Edinburgh, EH6 7EL	0131-554-5488	0131-554-7689
Shetland The Knab Knab Road Lerwick Shetland, ZE1 0AX	01595-696712	01595-692160
Marine Accident Investigation Branch 1st Floor Carlton House Carlton Place Southampton, SO15 2DZ	023-8039-5500 24 hour accident report 023-8023-2527	023-8023-2459
Ports Division DETR Department of Environment, Transport & the Regions Ports Division First Floor Great Minster House 76 Marsham street London, SW1P 4DR	020-7890-5089 020-7271-4474	020-7676-2188 020-7271-4485

Appendix 7.
Additional environmental impact information

The following text has been incorporated from the Environment Agency internal document *Scoping guidance for the environmental assessment of projects — generic impacts of construction works* (as available at the time of publication). The intention, as stated in the main text, is not to provide guidance on the environmental impact caused by construction works but rather to emphasise the potential impact that the environment will have on the construction process. To this end, the following issues have been listed to prompt consideration.

A7.1. GENERIC IMPACTS OF CONSTRUCTION WORK

This checklist has been produced to show how a development may affect the water environment (Table A7.1). Environment Agency concerns are listed under Issues; consultation is recommended to discuss precise requirements peculiar to a specific location. Additional checklists have been prepared for associated activities and are listed at the end of this document. Further guidance notes are available to provide greater detail where required.

Table A7.1.   Generic impacts of construction work (Environment Agency)

Issues	Sources of impact	Potential impacts
Surface Water Hydrology/ Hydraulics	Soil excavation, removal, storage	Changed surface water runoff Riparian drainage affected
	Soil compaction	Changed surface water runoff Changed magnitude of flooding Changed duration of flooding
	Laying of impervious surfaces (including roads)	Changed surface water runoff Changed flow velocities Changed magnitude of flooding Changed frequency of flooding Changed duration of flooding Changed flow regime Riparian drainage affected
	Drainage	Changed flow velocities
	In-channel works/channel diversion	Changed flow velocities
Channel morphology/sediments	Riparian soil Excavation/movement/loss of trees	Changed bank/bed stability Degradation/erosion of bed or banks Change of platform/siltation Deposition/siltation Changed suspended sediment load Changed bed load Sediment contamination
	In-channel works — piling, piers, bridges, vehicle movements	Degradation/erosion of bed or banks Disturbance to bed forms (pools, riffles) Deposition/siltation Changed channel size Changed suspended sediment load Changed bed load
	Channel realignment/diversion	Changed bank/bed stability Degradation/erosion of bed or banks Deposition/siltation Change of bed slope Change of platform/pattern Disturbance to bed forms (pools, riffles) Changed channel size
	Laying of impervious surfaces	Deposition/siltation Degradation/erosion of bed or banks Changed suspended sediment load Changed bed load

Table A7.1.   continued

Estuarine/coastal morphology	Structures and groynes	Changed erosion/sedimentation patterns
Groundwater hydraulics	Excavation	Changed flow
	Dewatering	Changed flow Change in water-table (level)
	Laying of impervious surfaces	Changed infiltration Change in water-table (level) Barrier to flow Change in pressure potential
	Structure	Changed flow Changed direction of flow
Surface-water quality	Storage and use of chemicals, fuel/oil, cement, etc., accidental spillage, vandalism and unauthorised use, site management including sanitation and sewerage	Changed in quality Chemical pollution Rubbish/trash Organic pollution Change in oxygen content Microbial contamination Changed turbidity Changed dilution capacity Nutrient enrichment Change in electrical conductivity/ pH acidifcation
	Earthworks	Changed turbidity Re-suspension of contaminated sediments
	Disturbance of contaminated land	Chemical pollution Organic pollution Rubbish/trash
	Laying of impervious surfaces	Changed turbidity
	Tree removal	Change in quality Nutrient enrichment
	In-channel works	Changed turbidity Organic pollution
	Channel realignment/diversion	Changed dilution capacity upstream
	Dewatering	Changed dilution capacity Changed turbidity Change in residence/flushing time
	Balancing ponds	Change in quality Changed turbidity

Table A7.1. continued

Issues	Sources of impact	Potential impacts
Groundwater quality	Soil excavation, removal, storage	Change in quality
	Concrete below water table, piling works for foundations	Change in quality Chemical pollution Organic pollution
	Storage and use of chemicals fuel/oil, etc.	Change in quality Chemical pollution Organic pollution
	Pumping	Chemical pollution Movement of contaminated water
	Disturbance of contaminated land	Chemical pollution Organic pollution
Aquatic ecology	Construction (including in-channel works) and associated works/laying of impervious surfaces	Altered habitat Loss of habitat Changed fish biomass Changed animal biomass Changed plant biomass Changed invertebrate biomass Changed species diversity Loss of sensitive species Effect on fish behaviour Change in fish community Effect on fish spawning Fish kill
	Channel realignment/ culverting/diversion	Altered habitat Changed invertebrate biomass Changed plant biomass Effects on fish spawning Loss of sensitive species Changed species diversity
	Dewatering	Altered habitat Changed plant biomass Changed invertebrate biomass Changed species diversity Loss of sensitive species
	Balancing ponds	Altered habitat Changed invertebrate biomass Loss of sensitive species
Terrestrial ecology	Fuel and chemical usage, site preparation and land take (including access roads, car parks, disposal/storage of soil, and other associated works)	Pollution through food chain Changed habitat Loss of wildlife habitat Tree removal Disturbance of sensitive species Changed species diversity Wetland change Illegal species imported

Table A7.1.   continued

Human-related	In-channel structures	Changed flood risk Disruption to commercial navigation
	Dewatering	Changed water resouce
	Channel realignment	Changed flood risk Changed abstraction rights
	Machinery operation, piling	Change in noise levels Increased vibration
	Traffic	Safety risk Change in noise level Disrupted access
	Site security and safety restrictions	Alterations to access
Land use change	Land take	Loss of riparian land
	Construction of buildings, car parks, etc.	Increased urban area Restriction to future developments
	Tree clearance	Deforestation
Visual amenity	Earthworks, construction	Altered aesthetic value
Recreation-related	Site security and safety restriction, permanent works	Alterations to access Disruption to users of water environment
	In-channel, works and structures	Disruption to users of water environment
Heritage and archaeology	Site preparation, excavation and land take	Disturbance and damage of known/unknown features Change to historic landscape

A7.1.1. References

Environment Agency documents

National Rivers Authority (NRA). (1992). *Policy and practice for the protection of groundwater.* Environment Agency, Rivers House, Waterside Drive, Aztec West, Almondsbury, Bristol, BS12 2UD.

NRA. (1994). *Contaminated land and the water environment.* Report of the NRA. Water Quality Series, No. 15. HMSO Environment Agency, Rivers House, Waterside Drive, Aztec West, Almondsbury, Bristol, BS12 2UD.

NRA. *Pollution Prevention Guidance 1, General guide to the prevention of pollution of controlled waters.* Environment Agency, Rivers House, Waterside Drive, Aztec West, Almondsbury, Bristol, BS12 2UD.

External publications

English Nature. (1994). *Roads and nature conservation. Guidance on impacts, mitigation and enhancement.* English Nature, Peterborough.

Forestry Commission. *Creating new native woodlands.* Bulletin 112. Rodwell, J.S. HMSO.

Larkin, P. A. (1984). A commentary on Environmental Impact Assessment for large projects affecting lakes and streams. *Can. J. Fisheries and Aquatic Science*, **41**, No. 7, 1121–1127.

Ministry of Agriculture Fisheries and Food (MAFF). (1999). *Handbook for the assessment of the hydraulic performance of environmental channels.* Report SR490. MAFF, London.

Renger, M. (1994). *Built environment, in environmental assessment; a guide to the identification, evaluation and mitigation of environmental issues in construction schemes.* Construction Industry Research and Information Association (CIRIA), 6 Storey's Gate, Westminster, London.

Department of the Environment. (1994). *PPG23 Planning and pollution control.* HMSO, London.

English Nature. (1994). *Nature conservation in environmental assessment.* English Nature, Peterborough.

Appendix 8.
Data sources and techniques for predicting tidal water level and wave conditions at a specified location

Tables A8.1–A8.5 provide a summary of data sources and techniques for predicting tidal water level and wave conditions at specified locations.

Table A8.1. Summary of methods available for predicting wind for construction works

Data output	Method	Information supplied by	Information best processed by	Comments	Outline cost of prediction
Wind atlases/ design guidelines	*Wind atlas: European wind atlas*, RISO National Laboratory (1989)	RISO National Laboratory (1989)	All	Atlas aimed at use for wind energy on land rather than coastal construction use. It is not site specific and may not contain the information in the ideal form	<£500 (cost of tables only)
	Wind atlas: Environmental parameters on the United Kingdom	Department of Energy	All	Provides useful extreme information on offshore wind statistics in the UK for maximum 1:50 year maximum wind speed	<£500 (cost of tables only)
	BS 6399: Part 2, *Loading buildings, Code of Practice*	BSI	All	Provides useful extreme information for land sites in the UK	<£500 (cost of tables only)
	UK Met. Office Model	Met. Office and authorised consultants	Met. Office and authorised consultants	Reliable and inexpensive source of offshore wind conditions	<£500
	Analysis of measured data	Met. Office, airports, wind records	Met. Office and consultants	More accurate than synthetic data but usually needs to be modified for use over water	<£1000

Table A8.2. Summary of methods available for predicting wave heights for construction sites

Data output	Method	Information supplied by	Information best processed by	Comments	Outline cost of prediction
Offshore wave heights (used as a basis to predict inshore conditions)	*Wave atlas: environmental parameters on the UK*	Department of Energy	All	Provides useful extreme information on offshore wave statistics in the UK for maximum 1:50 year maximum wave	<£500 (cost of tables only)
	Wave atlas: wave climate atlas of the British Isles	Institute of Oceanographic Sciences (now Southampton Oceanographic Centre)	All	Provides useful annual, spring, summer, autumn and winter offshore significant wave heights exceeded for 10%, 25%, 50% and 75% of the period and also the most common annual wave period. However, data is offshore and will have to be transferred inshore	<£500 (cost of tables only)
	Synthetic wave data (Met. Office Model and other sources)	Met. Office and consultants	Met. Office and authorised consultants	Synthetic wave data including that generated by the Met. Office. European wave model provides a reliable and inexpensive source of offshore conditions. A catalogue of data around the UK coast is given in HR 1995	<£1000 (data only)

Table A8.2.   continued

Data output	Method	Information supplied by	Information best processed by	Comments	Outline cost of prediction
	Wave measurements		Consultants	Time series data. Only really useful for validation of numerical models. Information listed in BODC* & HR 1998	<£1000 if already in existence
	Visual wave observation data	Met. Office	Consultants	Inexpensive, but only really useful in undeveloped areas of the world	>£1000
	Remote sensed data	Satellite imagery processing suppliers	Consultants	Limited use for coastal works due to insufficient detail and also wave period and direction are not available	<£1000
Inshore wave heights	Nomographs		All/consultants	Cheap and quick method of estimating inshore waves based on offshore conditions but limited use on complex bathymetry and climates	<£1000
	Numerical models	Met. Office and consultants	Consultants	Usually required because of complex bathymetry and coastline and mixed transformation processes, but more accurate	>£1000

*British Oceanographic Data Centre (BODC), Bidston Observatory, Bidston, Prenton, CH43 7RA.
E-mail: BODCmail@ccms.ac.uk, Website: www.bodc.ac.uk

Table A8.2. *continued*

Wave disturbance in sheltered locations	Numerical models	Consultants	Consultants	Usually the most reliable method of establishing wave conditions in sheltered locations	>£5000

Table A8.3. *Summary of methods available for predicting water levels for construction sites*

Data output	Method	Information supplied by	Information best processed by	Comments	Outline cost of prediction
Normal water level predictions	Admiralty tide tables	Admiralty	All	1. Cheap and quick method for approximating normal, and extreme levels for planning purposes 2. Tide tables do not include surge and other components but usually provide sufficient information for tender and site planning 3. Information may have to be interpreted from nearby prediction points	<£500 (cost of tables only)
	Tide table software	Software houses	All	1. Computerised version of the above 2. Can provide automated data useful for daily planning of the works	<£1000

Table A8.3.   continued

Data output	Method	Information supplied by	Information best processed by	Comments	Outline cost of prediction
Extreme water level prediction	*Surge maps: Environmental Parameters on the United Kingdom*, Department of Energy	Department of Energy	All	Provides useful extreme-information water-level statistics in the UK for maximum 1:50-year maximum surge level	<£500 (cost of tables only)
	Published data	Proudman Oceano-graphic Laboratories (POL, 1995)	All	Cheap and quick method for estimating extreme levels for planning and design of temporary works. Data usually available for 1:10-year to 1:10 000-year return periods	<£500 (cost of tables only)

Table A8.4.   Summary of methods available for predicting joint wave and water level probabilities

Data output	Method	Information supplied by	Information best processed by	Comments	Outline cost of prediction
Single joint probabilities	Desk assessment	Consultants	Consultants	Crude but useful for examining realistic joint probabilities	<£1000
Systematic capture of joint probabilities	Computational assessment	Consultants	Consultants	Comprehensive method for examining joint probabilities. Probably too expensive for use in most temporary works but essential for major permanent works	>£5000

Table A8.5. Types of real-time forecasting information available

Type of information	Method	Source	Information best processed by	Comments	Outline cost
Weather trends	Weather trends	Local information	All	Local people, such as fishermen who have a working knowledge of the area can provide useful hints on trends in wave conditions given a certain condition. Predictions may not be scientifically exact but they will give an indication of when problems may occur	Free
Extreme water levels	Flood alerts	Environment Agency	All	Environment Agency analyses forecast data and issues flood alerts when there is a risk of flooding in certain areas. Flood alerts are currently graded from yellow to red, but this system is under review	Free
	Storm tide warning service	UK Met. Office	All	A flood forecasting service funded by MAFF. A tidal model is run alongside the weather forecasting model, to predict storm surges. When the predicted total water level (i.e. astronomical tide plus surge) exceeds a given threshold for any particular division of coast, then a warning is issued	Free

Table A8.5. continued

Type of information	Method	Source	Information best processed by	Comments	Outline cost
Extreme water levels and offshore wave heights	On-line services	UK Met. Office	UK Met. Office/ consultants	The Met. Office provides an on-line phone and fax weather forecast service. Designed specifically for the building and construction industry, the service provides regional or site specific weather information ideal for day to day operations. As well as a standard package, tailor-made services can also be provided (see Samphire Hoe example in Box 3.5). Provides deep water forecast data up to 36 hours ahead, which may be useful in planning site activities. MAFF and NRA funded a study to assess the use of this type of data, in conjunction with local wave transformation modelling, for operational use at the coast. This offshore information can be transferred inshore by consultants	<£500
Inshore wave conditions	Wave conditions			Site specific	>£5000

Index

Page numbers in italics refer to figures, boxes and tables.